MY LIFE WITH BELLE

For Vicki with love from Juliet

Judith Ravenscroft (born 1947) has published stories in *London Magazine* and in several journals and anthologies. In 2001 she won a Society of Authors prize for a short story. She lives in London.

MY LIFE WITH BELLE

Judith Ravenscroft

LENZ
books

First published by
Lenz books, London

Copyright © Judith Ravenscroft, 2010

The right of Judith Ravenscroft to be identified as
the author of this work has been asserted by her in
accordance with the Copyright, Designs and Patents
Act of 1988

A CIP catalogue record for this book is available
from the British Library

ISBN 978-0-9564760-0-5

Printed and bound in Great Britain by
CPI Antony Rowe, Chippenham and Eastbourne

For Timothy Hyman

'... walking, a mode of exercise to which the sufferers from this malady are in general partial...'
(Dr James Parkinson, 1817)

Beginnings

On a morning walk I paused at the top of the steps leading down to the canal to take in the view. It was the darkest time of the year. Trees and tangled undergrowth, the slick of water, all continued bleak. I walked along the towpath to the next bridge, crossed the canal, and returned on the opposite side. As I reached the foot of the steep path that led back up to the road, a black-clad figure emerged from the gloom and bore down on me, pressing forward like the masthead of a noble ship. His face was blank – skin and bones, empty of personality – and he had a doomlike air. But then, as he passed, this apparition looked searchingly at me, seeking and holding my gaze.

That was one beginning, a few days before Victor left for America. A second came just before his return, when a delicate grey light signalled, if not the end of winter, at least the coming of spring. Descending the hill at the back of the house to walk into town, I felt elated, taken out of myself, and threw my head back to offer my face to the gentle air – until I started to topple over, as if unbalanced by a tug from behind. Returning to consciousness, I was able to right myself.

The streets were quiet at that hour, in the early afternoon; the houses, pairs of stucco villas, appeared abandoned, their windows staring blankly, and I passed no one until reaching the main road at the foot of the hill. There, cars hurtled past as I waited at the lights, but pedestrians were few until I reached the streets around the university. Now I was no longer taken up by the light and the air, but took note of the people, their faces, tense, self-absorbed, their bodies pressing forward as mine did, occupying its space and respecting that of others with an intuition based on long experience. Only the tourists got in the way, unsure of themselves, of where they were going, lacking any sense of their own rhythms as well as others', children in the ways of London.

A friend, Alice, was waiting for me under the portico of the British Museum. As we embraced I felt myself stiffen, become unsteady, again as if I might topple, and shuffled my feet.

Alice asked: 'What is it?'

'I'm just a bit stiff.' I easily steadied myself, and shrugged off my sense of an alien force.

Waiting

I saw Victor off at Heathrow. As we walked across a huge concourse crowded with passengers for the night flights, I burst into tears. It took me by surprise as much as it did Victor. I pressed my face to his chest so that people couldn't see me, and he hugged me as I tried to get a hold on myself and blubbered that I just felt emotional, and it was nothing he had to take seriously. I said the tears had come as a physical response to tension and didn't indicate a terrible sorrow even if normally I wept rarely.

We sat in a restaurant and Victor ate something and we both drank tea. He looked at me keenly once or twice to see if I'd controlled my tears, or perhaps just to note the evidence of tears on my face. Soon, since there was nothing else to do, he decided to go through customs. I walked with him to the gate. We hugged, and he turned and walked off, and just as he reached the screen beyond which I wouldn't be able to see him I called his name and he turned to me. He looked bewildered, as if he couldn't understand what was happening, that he was going to America and I was not. He smiled wanly at me and then he was gone.

I turned away too and made for the exit, and as I walked along a tunnel towards the trains I began to cry again. I stopped and got out my glasses and put them on in the hope that they would hide my tears. In the train I opened my book (Constant's *Adolphe*) and began to turn the pages, taking in little. But by the time I got off at Kings Cross I was engaged enough to comprehend whole sentences.

That hadn't been the end of our parting. Soon after I got home, I was sitting at a loss in the living-room when Victor phoned from the airport to say that he felt as if he was going down with flu. There was a catch in his throat and he felt unwell and wondered if he ought to cancel the trip. I tried to encourage him, and later he told me that what I'd said, something about a few days' flu not being much in the context of a two-month trip, had helped him, but I felt upset that there was nothing I could do for him when he was on his own and distressed, and I asked myself how I could possibly have let him go off without me. I was pleased to hear his voice one more time, but when our conversation was over and I put down the phone I wept again.

When I rang him next day in America he sounded cheerful. His throat was troubling him, but not too badly. He had slept on the plane and arrived feeling better than when he left. He'd seen a doctor and was taking some pills. Now he was with his very good friends. I didn't know these friends, and I felt a tiny stab of jealousy. He'd forgotten his fears at the airport, while I had been living with them ever since. I was still here, in London, in our flat in Finsbury, and he had moved there, thousands of miles to another continent, another time zone, another consciousness. I found it difficult to catch up with him, and perhaps he found it difficult, after the sudden transition, to recall what he'd left behind. But at least he'd arrived and was into the swing of things, and I could settle down to his absence.

That same evening, my friend Anna phoned to see how it had gone, Victor's departure, and how I was feeling. She asked me to visit her in the country, and I said I couldn't envisage leaving London. As I explained it to her, I thought I'd worry if I went away, about Victor, about the flat, about what might happen to both in my absence. Anna, who also found it difficult to leave home, for different reasons, understood my qualms but pointed out that she was on the phone and only an hour's train journey from London, so I could return quickly if I had to, as quickly as if I'd just gone to tea with a friend in south London. But not at night, I thought, which anyway missed the point, I wasn't worried about real possibilities but about ontological fears. Still, I wanted to see Anna, and for friendship's sake I would go.

An artist we knew had a private view of his work in a gallery in town. Victor had asked me to attend, and partly I did so for his sake, but I also wanted to test my resolve to live in the world while he was in America rather than hide myself away (as was my tendency) – even if private views were generally an ordeal for me.

When I got there I couldn't see anyone I knew and my one thought was to speak to the artist and leave. I refused a glass of wine, and began to make my way through the crowd. I kept having to apologise to people for getting in between them when they were talking, and then stepping sideways into someone else. Eventually I found myself at the edge of a group round the artist and waited for a chance to greet him.

For what seemed a long time, so that I became self-conscious, he resolutely avoided my eye, though I had the feeling he knew I was standing there. But then, as the person he was mainly talking to moved off, I stepped forward and he said hello. I told him Victor was away in America, and he said yes, of course, he'd known he was going, lucky man, and how he'd like to be there rather than here, anywhere rather than here, laughing. I said he seemed to be managing fine and it was a great show, though I'd have to return when it was quieter to see it properly. He thanked me, and then a gushy man interrupted to say how he must meet someone or other, and so I said goodbye.

Feeling relieved, I tried to look at the pictures. But as usual at such occasions I found it impossible to make much of the work. Either the crush forced me too close to the paintings, or if I stepped back people got in front of me. I continued to feel self-conscious, not wanting to cut anyone I knew, or on the other hand to look around me in case my eye met someone else's and I would have to greet them and would feel stuck to them, or would make them feel stuck to me.

But then I met a woman I knew. I told her it was like meeting a long-lost friend, and she laughed and asked where Victor was. I explained, and the woman, who was called Sasha, said that this kind of thing was always bad but on one's own it was torture. Then her companion came up, a man I felt uneasy with, and the conversation became awkward, and after a while I left.

On my way home on the bus I wondered why I'd made myself go to the private view which I'd been dreading all day. By now I should have developed the confidence to do what I wanted, to respect the way I was and live by it. It would have been good enough, and not discourteous, to see the pictures another time and send the artist a card.

I walked to work down the hill at the back of the house and then more or less in a straight line through

Bloomsbury, finally taking a left turn into Soho. I was walking towards Russell Square one morning – spindly winter trees beneath a grey sky filled the space ahead –, when a dark anger took hold of me. At that moment, a week or two into his absence, I felt abandoned by Victor. It seemed to me that he'd left me to do an unpleasant secretarial job, which I'd taken on because of our financial difficulties, to supplement my earnings from freelance work as an editor, and that somehow he'd managed to escape to America while I was left behind in my dreary, drudging existence. As I walked along a phrase kept repeating itself in my mind again and again: how could he do this to me, how could he do this to me, how could he do this to me.

Since ringing Victor just after he arrived in America I hadn't been able to make contact with him again. I knew which cities he was in and I knew the institutions he was lecturing at, but I didn't know where he was staying and so I hadn't been able to phone him. Later, he explained how difficult it had been, how he'd felt unable to ring long-distance from the private homes he was staying in and how he never had time to find a public phone because he was constantly being rushed by his highly organised hosts to the next appointment. For some reason I didn't, as I could have done, ring the institutions and track down the relevant person who could give me the phone number of the place where he was staying.

Before he left we had discussed my joining him for the Christmas holiday, and decided against it on the grounds of expense, wear and tear, and the difficulty of my fitting into his schedule halfway through. I thought it likely that I'd get there and he would have little time for me and so I'd hang about almost as alone as I was at home. I forgot these arguments as I walked round Russell Square, or at least as arguments they lost their force in the face of my anger and longing. But then, when it came to it, I didn't go, there was no point in going.

I finally spoke to Victor when he reached Denver, almost three weeks into his trip. I got through to him at once, and felt a catch in my throat as the familiar voice answered with a slightly impatient hello, as if he was in the middle of something and was irritated at being interrupted, and with his tone rising at the end into a question mark. 'Hel-*lo?*'

'Hi,' I replied, 'it's me.' And then, probably sounding a little histrionic, I said: 'I can't go on not speaking to you.' He seemed to laugh, unless what I heard was an intake of breath. I felt an enormous relief, to be able at last to hear his voice, so that I could place him in his hotel room in my imagination and he had some reality for me. No, he didn't look out on to a parking lot but on to ground that sloped down towards a frozen stream. He'd just come, he said, from having a swim in the pool. It was next to the place where people ate breakfast, idly watching the swimmers, on this occasion Victor and a small boy who splashed around a lot. It felt a little too public.

'A pool's a pool,' I said, wondering whether it would have been the deciding factor in my joining him in Denver; if I'd known about the pool I might definitely have gone.

The hotel was nothing special, and noisy at night because his room was above a bar. 'I tried to change it but there wasn't another one free.'

'So if I'd joined you, we would have had a double and I'd have saved you from sleepless nights.'

He laughed, uncertainly, as if he hadn't heard me, or hadn't got the point, but still picked up an edge in my voice and thought it safest not to inquire further. I asked if the sun was out, and it was and felt warm even though the snow was thick on the ground. That also sounded attractive to me, looking out of the window as I listened to him, at a drizzly afternoon.

He told me what had been happening to him, about the friends he'd seen, and about the lectures, which had been going well apart from one in which the computer had crashed and he'd had to speak without showing any images, and how his throat was better, though his voice became hoarse during lectures, and how people had been kind and hospitable and welcoming. Then he asked about me, and I told him about Belle, and after a few affectionate words we said goodbye.

Belle was Isabelle de Charrière, the great *epistolière* of the eighteenth century. I had come to her by way of *Adolphe*, Benjamin Constant's brilliant and disquieting story about a young man's seduction of an older, married woman, Ellénore, and her subsequent ruin and death. Adolphe tells how at first Ellénore resists his advances, but then succumbs, and how at the point of conquest his feelings begin to cool. He is too cowardly to tell her the truth, and when she leaves her husband and children for him, guilt and pity propel him into fleeing with her. He tries to do his duty by her, against the advice of his father and friends. Her recriminations turn inwards and, eventually, broken-hearted, she dies.

Ellénore's death was troubling. I couldn't see that aesthetics required such a harsh outcome, and I didn't entirely believe in Adolphe's declaration of anguish and guilt. I read in one source that Constant had based Ellénore on his old friend Isabelle de Charrière. Others insisted that the strongly individuated Belle bore little resemblance to his poor, compromised protagonist. Rather he may have had her in mind when, early on in his book, begun not long after Belle's death in 1805, Adolphe refers to the passing of an ageing woman whose exceptional intellect and tough morality powerfully influenced him at a young age. In any case, like others before me, I presumed to write a different ending for Constant's book.

Some friends rang from Holland to say they were coming to London for three days. I had never met this couple before but they were important friends, for I had corresponded with one of them for a couple of years as a result of some connection over writing. I felt nervous about their visit, handling it without Victor, as I generally let him take the lead at social occasions, while I held back; instead of taking responsibility, at least for my own friends, which I had done in the past, before Victor, but had since become lazy about.

I made an effort over dinner (chicken, fruit tart, cheese), taking some pleasure in it since I'd done no real cooking since Victor left. My friends brought wine and two pairs of thick, hand-knitted socks, for Victor and me, which were produced in the part of Holland they lived in. They laid themselves open with a generosity I did my best to match. Only one of them was Dutch; the other, the one I'd been writing to, Tom, was American. They lived quietly in a small town, where the Dutchman ran a research institute.

They asked me about Victor, about how I was managing without him. I was pleased to be asked in such a simple, direct way, and to be able to explain it, and to have them listen to my explanation without interjecting too much with their own comparable experiences. How I defined it to them was that I missed Victor, in that I felt the lack of him, his absence, and counted the weeks until his return, yet at the same time I carried on more or less as usual, a normality that was partly that of my daily life at that time and partly my experience of solitude before I met Victor.

I had lived alone for ten years, the whole period after leaving my parents' home. Finding myself alone again, I knew it would be easy to fall back into old, familiar ways. In the past, in the years of my aloneness before Victor, I often drank too much. I would come home from whatever job I was doing and open a bottle of wine and by the end of the evening I'd have finished it. Often in the morning I'd wake with a headache and a dry mouth and feeling queasy, and I generally had dark shadows under my eyes. Victor didn't like my drinking and so I stopped it. I still drank, and sometimes we split a bottle over dinner, but I no longer drank in the old way.

With the office closed for the holiday, I had a fortnight free to concentrate on Belle. I also arranged two or three fixed points of sociability which were as much as I thought I wanted. I planned to write every day, but despite the perfect conditions – of which Victor's absence was one – it went badly. With every morning session I seemed to go through the motions, as if it was something to be done because it had to be, as a point of honour rather than because it engaged or enriched me, or sharpened my understanding, which was why I did it in the first place. I felt I'd lost my sense of aspiration, my fervour, so that when I wasn't sitting at my desk banging out a few desultory words I was lying on the daybed reading books chosen not for their distinction or even their relevance to my own project but because they held my attention, story books that relied heavily on suspense. I became aware that the hopes I'd begun this period of Victor's absence with, hopes to lead a full and directed life even if I missed him, threatened to give way to a sense of marking time, whereby I passed the days numbly and pointlessly until his return. It was as if I'd given up the struggle, and somehow this came to seem, in the days between Christmas and New Year, as emblematic of my life in general. As if I had never found the stamina to keep on trying, and gave in too easily to discouragement. I felt humiliated by my mediocrity, a woman after all defined by a man, given meaning only by his presence.

Later I came to see the days around Christmas as marked mainly by their being at the fag end of the year, so that whether Victor had been there or not I would have experienced much the same loss of direction. Even at the time I had the dim sense that these days, which might or might not have been better managed, were just bad days to be got through and that once the new year had started my mood would become lighter.

My brother Simon invited me over on New Year's Eve. His wife Alison had asked her sisters, with their husbands and offspring. By the time I got there the food had been reduced to little more than a mess of smeared plates as if the company had ravenously devoured every crumb of food. I was struck, as I stood by the table and took in the room, by the force and vitality of this family compared to my own, which was so much quieter, even languid. Victor's family too made this sort of impression on me, and it was as if we'd chosen partners, my brother and I, to supplement our own depleted sources of vitality.

On my way home in a pre-ordered cab the driver asked me if I was going out to a party, and I said no, I was coming home from one. I laughed, but the driver seemed nonplussed. I asked him where he was from, and he said Zimbabwe; he had been in England for ten years, and had a university degree and a qualification in accountancy but had never been able to get a professional job. And so he drove a cab, and usually he took people to and from the airport, which was the journey he liked most because it reminded him that there was still a world outside England and one day he'd return to it. Soon, he said, there'd be an election in Zimbabwe and perhaps then the government would change and he could go home. All this had a chastening effect on me, for what was the two months of my separation from Victor compared with the ten years this man had been parted from his family and forced to work in menial jobs? But I didn't want my feelings of optimism, now that the new year had begun, to be undermined by the driver's tragedy, and so I said little and looked out of the window. I saw that the streets were very busy, full of good-natured crowds, and it occurred to me that it had been unnecessary to order a cab, I would have been perfectly safe on the tube and would probably have enjoyed the sense of uproarious camaraderie. Then I felt badly about the driver and turned to him again, but he no longer wished to unburden himself.

When I got home I found a message from Victor on the answering machine and immediately rang him back in his hotel room. As I was to remember it later, this was one of the best calls we had while he was in America, not because of anything particular that was said, but because of the ease with which we spoke. It was as if he wasn't thousands of miles away in a place I could only imagine, and that we weren't in the outlandish circumstance of being separated for weeks on end, but as if we'd seen each other only a day or two before, and would again shortly, and meanwhile we were passing the time of day. But we ended on a wistful note with the realisation which came quite suddenly towards the end of our conversation that we missed each other and it would be several more weeks before we were together again, assuming we would be, a rider I felt obliged to add, in my mind, not out loud, but like a good-luck charm, so as not to tempt fate.

I went to see Anna in the Kentish countryside. We took a long walk, setting out from her back door and making a great circle to end up at her front door. We walked round the edges of turfy fields, across heath-lands strewn with cow pats, through straggly copses; and we crossed a stream, jumping from one stone to another. It was as exhilarating in its way as a long walk in London, because of a feeling of unity with my surroundings, but without the particular sense in London of continuity with past generations of Londoners, which conferred a sort of immortality.

We talked about a book we had both read, a diary kept by an older woman, in her sixties, in a remote part of New England, where conditions through the winter were severe, with dangerous wildlife as well as deep frosts and wild storms, and she was constantly fighting a desperate loneliness, although she couldn't imagine living in any other way. I admired her, for her courage in being true to her reclusive character, even if it was a lifelong difficulty, and for the intensity of her concentration in every aspect of her life. Anna said that in her experience it was impossible to be reclusive in the country because every Tom, Dick, and Harry – none of them a soulmate – were forever barging in, and her concentration was continually undermined by her fear of crisis, or by actual crises, failures in the system brought on by inclement weather.

My back ached after such a long walk, my legs were tired, and Anna commented on my unfitness.

Later, we sat in front of a fire, which was a comfort against the threatening sounds of a wild night, and it felt good to be there with Anna, who was such a very good friend. But even so I felt restless and melancholy, anxious about my home, in case something was wrong there, more than about Victor, who seemed so far away, even more so because I myself was away from home, that I could barely conjure him in my mind.

It was on my way home from Anna's that I saw Belle's house. It appeared in the darkening valley below, so unexpected and so fleeting in its fragile, whitish elegance that it might have been a ghost, no sooner seen than lost as the bus plunged into a tunnel of trees. But then it came into view again, looming above us, on its solitary knoll. A house with a haunting beauty, perfect in its generous proportions, its soft pale pinkish stone, its wide-eyed windows that drew one in despite the drawn blinds, the closed gate, the darkness. I knew I would give it to Belle, never mind that it was in Kent, not Switzerland, and of a later time. I imagined dust sheets on the furniture, field mice running across bare wooden floors, an abandoned house, or a house that someone would come back to, that Belle would come back to, never to leave again.

In the days before Victor's return I tried to finish what I was writing (about Belle's first meeting with Constant in Paris; there was some mystery about why she had gone there, alone, without her husband, whom she seems to have left abruptly). I wasn't writing it for Victor and his being there or not was irrelevant to its completion. Partly I was just making a deadline to galvanise myself, but I also felt a strong desire to complete what I had worked on while Victor was away, to be able to draw a line underneath his absence and everything to do with it.

He was due back very early on a Saturday in March. On the Friday I went to the office as usual. That evening I went to bed early in order to be up by six-thirty in the morning. But I woke every half-hour through the night, and at last got up and made a pot of tea and had drunk it by the time I heard a taxi outside and going to the window saw Victor. And it was as if he was returning as he so often had before from a few days up north, until I opened the door and we hugged and I buried my face in the unfamiliar smells of another country.

A fate like lead

One early summer's day we walked, Victor and I, to the river, taking the street that curved with generous swathes down the hill from the Angel to Smithfield. Past St Paul's, we went down the steps to the riverside, where we stood at the balustrade, looking up and down stream and across to the old power station, which had become the Tate gallery, on the south bank. The water was still and grey, like the sky, and the view was big and wide, a great expanse of greyness, but pearly, pinkish, purply too.

We took a taxi home because I was troubled by an aching back.

My back almost stopped me going with friends on a long walk across the Heath. But the day was glorious – a sun you could feel on your back, a world that sparkled – and I wanted only to be out in it. We started in Highgate, walking down past the allotments into Kenwood, and across to Parliament Hill. Long before we halted for coffee I wanted to lie flat on the ground.

A friend lagged behind with me and asked what it was, this bad back, as if he didn't quite believe in it, it didn't correspond to what he knew of bad backs.

'And you're walking oddly,' he said, but couldn't define how it was. It was different, he said, it had changed. Perhaps I wore ill-fitting shoes?

At an exhibition of paintings, one image made a particular impression on me, a charcoal drawing of a man about to enter a cave. The black tones gave a certain ambiguity to the feeling of the man, who seemed both eager and fearful in relation to the cave, which perhaps he wasn't going to enter, because the dream, which was what the image felt like, would stop before he had to. If that had been my dream, I thought, I would have felt an inevitability about entering the cave, in which apprehension and curiosity and resignation were all mixed up.

And what with one thing and another I fell over, tripped, and couldn't save myself, or lost my balance – afterwards I couldn't reconstruct the circumstances, but remembered the cracking sound of bone on concrete as my knees hit the floor and the feeling that my whole world had given way.

A friend, mainly of Victor's, though I liked her too, had a birthday, and someone we didn't know gave a party for her. As the weeks passed and the date of the party came closer, I became agitated at what I had let myself in for. It became an enormous obstacle in my path, something I had to get past before I could regain my composure. I counted the weeks and days and hours until it would be over and I imagined how that would be, when we got home from the party, and I had survived it, how I'd lie in bed beside Victor, how relieved I'd feel, and we'd talk about what it had been like and then read a little before going to sleep.

We expected a real party, with more people than could sit round a table, enough people so that I could sit in a corner with just one, or if not, then at least I could leave after a couple of hours without anyone minding, rather than having to stick it out through two or three courses and coffee. But when I walked into the house and glanced into the dining room I saw at once that the round table had been laid for ten people. I looked at Victor, who wouldn't meet my eye, and I felt an acute stab of betrayal, whether by Victor or his friend or life I couldn't say. And then, though it wasn't too bad, because most people try to be friendly, and it's rare to meet a truly obnoxious person, it wasn't too good either, because I had very little to say to any of these people, who were from another world of business and banking, or if I did (and it's not impossible that if I'd been trapped in a lift with any one of them I would have got quite far) I couldn't say it with other people listening – which is the problem with dinners for a few people, the seminar problem, that you're expected to sing for your supper and feel ashamed if you don't. As it was, I kept losing the drift of the conversation, and sat as if struck dumb, and fearful lest someone require an opinion from me on whatever they were talking about, which had invariably escaped me.

The other person who wasn't having a very good time was our friend whose birthday it was. She looked as if she had wandered into the party by mistake, someone else's birthday party, and was baffled by the attention she was getting. Baffled too, the other guests and our hosts stopped attending to her, and mostly, like me, she sat in silence. Later, she told Victor she had taken some comfort from my presence, since I too seemed at a loss. She said that she'd wanted to laugh when I reached out to pick some grapes from a bowl of fruit at the centre of the table and then abruptly withdrew my hand as if I'd realised I wasn't supposed to eat the grapes, that they were there for display.

Sometimes I found myself blaming Victor for involving me in social occasions with people I had nothing to say to, and he'd defend himself: you never knew when you might meet a new friend and if you didn't go to parties you never would; that conversation helped to clarify your views about things; that even if the talk seemed pointless it got you closer to the people you were talking to. 'You'd do better,' he advised me, 'to think about how other people strike you, rather than worrying about the impression you're making on them.' And: 'Let people know who you are instead of shutting yourself up.'

This time he agreed with me that it was a pointless occasion. And I had to agree with him: the futility of the party was unusual, something neither of us could have anticipated, and that we had both felt obliged to support our friend on her birthday and could hardly have refused. In the course of a life, Victor said, a person has to expect a few bad evenings.

He painted a picture which seemed to show how it was for me. He was leaping on to a bus, grabbing the pole with one hand to hoist himself on to the platform. Not everyone noticed the floundering figure on the right, the hesitant, fearful woman who wasn't sure whether she wanted to follow him, whether she had the courage to make the leap, and was weighing up the dangers, and obviously envisaging disaster: as he flew through the air she saw him fall, caught up in the wheels of the bus, mangled and dead. And he wanted her to follow.

Stiffness in my limbs, unsteadiness, a back that refused to get better. And a peculiar way of walking which neither I nor Victor nor anybody else could describe except in terms of its unfamiliarity. Later, someone would tell me that a normal gait is an even gait, that however a person might walk, each side was the same, and that I walked unevenly, as if I was two people, split down the middle. But at the time neither I nor anyone I asked could define what was odd about my walking. So I watched people in the street and walked behind them trying to imitate their walk, though I knew this to be futile, since everyone walked differently, and it was my own particular way that I had lost and wanted to regain, along with a state of thoughtlessness about walking as I made my way about London. Also, Victor commented that I kept saying how clumsy I was with my hands. (At that point I didn't include the apparition in my list of unexplained episodes, and I felt bound to challenge Victor's depiction of my fearfulness, but I wondered aloud about the pain in my deepest places, like a jagged ache through the root of me, coming two or three times and then not again.)

I had a theory of my own. A young man visited, the son of a friend, who had come to London to study. He told me about the course he was doing, that once he'd completed it and had a qualification then all sorts of doors would open for him. He'd get a job which would pay for a flat in town so that he wouldn't have to commute from the suburb he was living in now. He was full of optimism, in the way of people at the beginning of something new, especially if they're young.

As I was talking to him, I remembered a newspaper article I'd read about a young woman who had chosen to remain celibate and at twenty-six wrote a book about it. Celibacy, it seemed, was no longer something to be ashamed of as it had been in the days when it was called virginity and one didn't choose it. It seemed that lots of men had wanted to sleep with this young woman but she'd held off. And that, I thought, would make it much easier, to be able to boast of one's strength of character rather than admit to failure on the sexual front. I didn't say any of this to the young man (later I thought that if I had we might have had a more interesting conversation). It just passed through my mind as he spoke of his plans, perhaps because of the boy's optimism, his easy assumption that he'd find the job and flat he wanted, just as the young woman in the newspaper article seemed to know what she wanted to do and to do it. Perhaps that's what connected them in my mind, their youthful confidence, and my envy, an ageing woman's envy of the young.

That gave me one clue. A dream seemed to provide another: I'm standing pressed against a tree as if hiding. Voices call me. I know what they have to tell me, I've seen what was coming: my mother's struggle as she gasped for breath. I know and don't want to hear it said out loud. So I press one ear against the knobbly bark and with my hand cup the other. Even as I stand there, I think that I can't remain clamped to that tree for ever. Next, an open door and, in the room beyond, a window ablaze with sunlight. I enter and see a young woman lying naked on the bed. Smooth skin, pure lines, limbs askew with a child's awkwardness – and dead.

'That's not my mother!' I say in the knowledge that this isn't the body of a woman who has carried children but a girl's that has borne none.

Someone brushes past with a jug of water and a towel, and begins to wash the corpse. Smooth, delicate hands go about their work. Under my eyes, they become red and rough, and marked, like my own hands, by the blemishes of age. Later, I would give this dream to Belle, when in her disconsolate middle age I imagined her thoughts returning to her mother's death. Its meaning seemed obvious: we were burying our youth and suffering the first infirmities of old age.

Months passed. The hot summer gave way to a sweetly melancholy autumn. I sat on a bench in the garden of our square and lapped up the sun, knowing that soon we'd get no warmth from it for months to come. The anxiety that had settled on me seemed to be in abeyance. I believed my aches and pains to be nothing but a temporary stage of life. All was well – but then, on my way home one evening, walking along Theobald's Road, I again encountered the apparition that months before had passed me on the canal – the same masklike face, neither young nor old, neither ugly nor handsome. Again he seemed to emerge out of a dim and misty gloom. He stared at me, and I felt unsettled and tried to avoid his eye.

Next, an old acquaintance telephoned and said, 'I heard you were sick.' His words shocked me. I wanted to protest his misinformation, as if it hadn't occurred to me, as apparently it had to others, that I was ill. In bookshops, surreptitiously, I began to look for a label for my ailments but couldn't find them exactly described. A doctor supplied it, after journeying round my body with the fluency of a musician practising his instrument. Moving on from one part to the next, no pauses, but a continuous, concentrated proceeding: eyes, mouth, arms, legs, extremities – he peered, tapped, manipulated, and pronounced: the malady of Doctor P.

*

What I remember now of the days and weeks that followed has little feeling. It's as if the shock of it numbed my memory, so that though I can see myself doing what I did, and hear myself saying what I said, I don't feel what I felt.

I remembered a fancy of my mother's. As a young woman, looking out of a window of her childhood home, she had seen a large young girl with her chin in the air like a camel, loping towards her across the street. Years later, suddenly (while sitting in the waiting room of a dentist in the same street), she remembered the girl and believed she recognised her as me. 'You came from the future' was how she had put it, laughingly, but it always made me uneasy. If the future can appear in the past, and since as we all know the past can resonate in the future, then there was no escape: as she lay dying I knew without a doubt that my mother expected me soon to follow her. As I approached her bed, I felt the force of her will, the draw of her charisma, and it took every mite of my strength to resist her. She would not be patient, she was biding her time only until my spirit was weak, and then she would call me.

I watched myself closely. Through that winter and into spring I always walked the same daily route to the canal and back so as to note any change in the time I took, how breathless I became while climbing the steep hill up to the road from the water, how tired I felt when I got home. Sometimes I was slow and listless, and at other times I took a minute or two less and felt well at the finish. There seemed to be no pattern, or steady deterioration.

People go on, the doctor had said, for ten years. Or fifteen. Even twenty. Before what? Death? Before my condition became severe? Victor and I thought of the friend who was dying in those days, how grateful he'd be for ten years. Ten years was a long time. A decade. It was unimaginably longer than six months, say. And perhaps there'd be more.

I sought information but then found I couldn't bear to read it. In the library I looked out the famous essay in which Doctor P. described the disease his name was given to. It made harrowing reading and I got no further than page four ('its last stage...the wished for release') before fleeing.

Then, there were other people, those whose response seemed to me inadequate, because they said too much or not enough, or nothing at all, were too empathetic or insufficiently so, though what I wanted I had no idea, and perhaps when someone made the right response it was just chance. There were also the people I believed had done me down, the 'I'll show them' people, the snubbers and dismissers, the jeerers and sneerers. Now, with my mind's eye, I saw pity in their faces, pity tinged with triumph.

I came to believe it had always been within me, the malady: a stickiness in manner and mind, a lack of stamina, episodes of clumsiness and inarticulacy, all of which, slowly, over many years, grew and coalesced until they ceased to be qualities of being and became signs of disease. It seemed important to be able to trace its origins to the distant past, to look for clues in a place and time that were beyond my influence. I dreamt that a young girl tugged at my arm for attention. She put her mouth to my ear to tell me her name, which wasn't the usual sort of name but consisted of a sentence of several words. I immediately forgot her words, either in the dream or when I woke, but clearly she had something to tell me, something I needed to know.

I dug out a photo of the child I once was: standing ankle deep in the shallows of a sea, hands on hips, head held to one side, eyes squinting in the sun. It brought a memory of youthful grace. My eyes fixed wide, I see the sandy seabed arranged in elegant swathes, dappled with gentle ridges; and dead-white as if boneless hands, mine, cutting through the limpid water. I reach upwards, kicking my legs hard, arms outstretched above my head to break the surface, an elegant streak cutting cleanly through the water, and causing hardly a ripple.

I looked again at the photo of my child self. For what? Signs of illness, or frailty? or defiance and resilience? It told me nothing.

One night, I lay flat out, trancelike, feeling my arms and legs as blocks of wood in which the forms of my limbs were only faintly suggested. I experienced myself as a tiny kernel encased in an alien body. I knew that if I moved I could break the spell, but wanted to see where it took me, this fullness and rigidity, this absence of subtle variation. It took me nowhere, allowing me no redemptive hallucinations, passing off of its own accord, so that shapeliness was restored to me. The episode brought a phrase to mind, one that I'd just read in a story by Büchner, and now repeated to myself again and again: a fate like lead, a fate like lead, a fate like lead.

My Belle

Portrait

Reddish hair, high colour, wide open faces: the parents, cousins, are of a kind, their children shaped in the same mould. The mother, at one end of the table, smiles indulgently, at no one in particular. The father, at the other, appears to think only of chewing. Neither takes any notice of two young boys who, on and off their chairs, are teasing a cat, though an older sister looks their way and may soon restrain them. An adult son sits beside his mother and raises a glass to his lips. And, next to the father, a young woman we know to be Belle laughs challengingly at the brother who's her favourite. This is Ditie, and from his place down the table he seems to look up at Belle, at the centre of the picture, their star. Her gifts are prodigious; by now (she is nineteen), as well as being fluent in French and her native Dutch, she has learnt English, translated Horace from Latin, studied mathematics, made music, written poems and many letters – and is composing her first novella. She is said to be a beauty, but here what is notable is her liveliness, and an almost quivering sensitivity – excitement, anticipation – in the curves of her profile.

D'Hermenches

Belle met d'Hermenches in The Hague, at a ball at the duke of Brunswick's. He wore a black band round his head, for reasons unknown. He was famous for it, so nobody bothered to explain what it was for, whether it was just an idiosyncratic accessory, or he believed it helped his chronic headaches. He would have made an impression, even without his reputation – as a soldier and man of letters, and as a rake. It was also said that he was a friend of Voltaire.

He stood alone, detached, watching the crowded room with aplomb. Belle seized her chance and introduced herself. 'You're not dancing, sir?'

'I've never learnt to dance and talk at the same time. And I prefer to talk – when I can find anyone to engage with me.'

'That's just how I feel about it.'

'Yes, I noticed how you worked your way across the room. You must have greeted twenty people – and apparently found no one to your liking.'

'I haven't got time to waste.'

'But you have a lifetime. Look at me. I'm more than halfway through and still stand about watching the world. You're in too much of a hurry.'

'Holland isn't the world, it's a backwater where you're amusing yourself for a few days as a researcher might. It's not the world for me either, but it's almost the only part of it I've seen and I know it far better than I want to.'

'And when you catch sight of a stranger across the room you make a point of going over to him.'

'I'm told you're a friend of Voltaire.'

'Ah – you admire him?'

'Not his new book. It's a potboiler.'

'Is that what they say here?'

'I have no idea what they say here. I myself think it's a potboiler.'

'You're wrong. It's a difficult book, misunderstood by those who are prejudiced against him.'

'What kind of argument is that? To say I'm wrong because I hold a different opinion from you. To call me prejudiced because I disagree with you.'

She didn't like the way he laughed, that he was apparently laughing at her, and she turned to leave. He took her arm to hold her back, and in the course of the evening he offered something – friendship, or a correspondence, it's not clear exactly what, but she understood he wanted to continue their exchange. Then she didn't hear from him. Several weeks went by, and rather than let him go she again made the first move.

'I will not dissemble,' she began her letter – but then did. She was writing because she'd failed to seek him out to say goodbye, and believed in observing the courtesies. She expected no answer, indeed urged him to burn her silly, girlish note; but, on the other hand, she would hate him (no less) if he failed to honour the trust she was placing in him. Hadn't he claimed to want her confidence? – he had said he desired it ardently – and she reminded him too of his promise to be sincere, his assurance that she had nothing to fear from him.

And then, having dared, and elicited a response, she lost her nerve, wanted to call a halt to the whole thing. D'Hermenches, at thirty-seven, was seventeen years older than her. Perhaps someone, possibly her brother Ditie, told her that the sickly wife he left at home in the country was not the mother of the daughter who sometimes travelled with him. Belle came clean: she risked her reputation, already there were rumours, potential husbands would be put off.

He replied with some memorable phrases: 'the blaze of my friendship', 'the affinity of our souls'. And what kind of suitors were these, he wanted to know, that they objected to her corresponding with the one person capable of appreciating her genius?

She wrote one more letter, and then another – and felt ridiculous, threatening to stop writing to him even as she continued. So she withdrew her objections and they settled into it. Supreme practitioners of the epistolary art, ardent students of the human condition, over fifteen years they opened up their lives and thoughts one to the other, for their own delight and ours.

Marriage

She didn't want to talk about marriage, she wrote to d'Hermenches, but when he pressed her she admitted she needed a husband because only then could she be free. She wanted to live without constraints, at liberty to study and write what she pleased, to choose her own friends, to educate her children. She couldn't do this on her own – it would distress her parents – and her husband must willingly give her her head.

D'Hermenches, a fixer by nature, came up with the marquis. What he seemed to have in mind was a threesome. He envisaged their perfect happiness – not just hers and the marquis's but his own too, as if he'd be marrying her by proxy.

Just in time, she discovered passion, or its absence. Away from the marquis she imagined the one, and when she was with him, which occurred rarely, she experienced the other. She blamed herself, she said to d'Hermenches: she was awkward, clumsy. But his friend's pursuit of her was altogether too tepid for a woman who felt her chastity as a deprivation. She wanted to hear no more about husbands, if she needed one she'd find him herself.

Then her mother died. They had all questioned the inoculation – Belle's father, the doctor, her older brother Eric – but Belle's certainty, her contempt for their ignorance, her youthful embrace of what was new, had overborne their doubts. Only her mother trusted her in the matter of the cowpox – and died of the fever that resulted. And Belle's father blamed her. Possibly. It's been suggested. And to me seems likely.

After the burial her father was inconsolable. He glanced up at Belle when she entered the room, his expression distracted, as if he hardly knew her, and at once turned away. Eric stood behind him, and taking his cue from his father also ignored her. Instinctively she looked to Ditie for reassurance – he opened his eyes wide, and she nodded slightly in response.

She walked over to her father, placed a hand on his shoulder, and when he looked up bent to kiss his forehead. He gestured, as if to say, yes, yes, but not now – and returned to his contemplation of the fire.

He didn't invite her, as the oldest daughter, to take her mother's place at table. Belle sat in her usual seat beside him until it occurred to her to move down the table and busy herself with her sister's children. One refused to eat and while Belle coaxed him the other gave morsels of food to the cat under the table. The cat jumped on to the child's lap and from there to the table. Their father looked up and gazed bewildered at the animal. Then, as he turned to Belle, his head jerked in a spasm – of what? It was more than ir- ritation. But surely he didn't hate her.

She took the children to visit her old nurse, wife of a harbour master on the coast. She walked beside the sea and, drenched by the waves, waited beneath vast, racing skies for her spirits to lift. But even the sea couldn't break the hold of her depression. She was there as carer to two young children, in conversation most of the day with them or her nurse. If she was going to be confined, let it not be as unwilling companion to a grieving and judging widower, in a home and world that imprisoned her.

D'Hermenches knew Charles de Charrière of old, came from the same corner of Switzerland. 'An excellent man, but...' He didn't list his failings, nor did Belle press him. They had books in common, which seemed good enough for her, even if Charles, her brothers' tutor, couldn't match her gifts and knew it: he wrote that he was like her pupil, that she made him forget his role as sage. Belle would continue to refer to him as the tutor long after he ceased to be one.

Charles's doubts were shared by d'Hermenches. Belle was attaching herself to a man who would always remain in her shadow and would come to resent it. And she, having soon exhausted anything that was interesting or surprising in him, would look in vain for stimulating relationships among his friends and neighbours. She had misunderstood her needs and was too impatient. All she thought of was getting out of her father's backwater. Couldn't she see that by marrying Charles she would simply plunge into another? Aged thirty, she could expect another thirty years in which to enjoy or endure her choice, 'and thirty years is a very long time'.

She hesitated. But then wrote to him to explain: after losing her mother she hadn't wanted to marry. But her family liked Charles, and so did she; he was a sincere and reasonable man, and he loved her without illusion. Besides, she was in an awkward situation at home. She could see no other way of changing it. And so she'd told her father she was ready to sign the contract that would formally engage her.

They had to curtail the honeymoon because of a condition she called her vapours, perhaps because no doctor was ever able to define it: a recurring indisposition, or perhaps a cyclical lowering of spirits. Her health would always bother her, but, instructed by her sisters-in-law, she found she liked domestic tasks and became expert at washing the household's linen – news that d'Hermenches must have received with disgust. Otherwise the main difference from her previous life, she wrote to him, was that she no longer always slept alone. Thus, she had settled into her new home, and declared herself delighted.

Mme de Charrière

I'm taller than her, and thinner – wrote Charles, of Belle. She's fair and I'm dark.

She speaks fast and holds nothing back. I prise the words out of myself and rarely manage more than a sentence at a time. In a foreign language, she becomes the part, throwing herself into look and gesture, as well as perfectly mimicking the sounds of the words, while I'm unable to be anyone but myself.

I love walking, but she hates it. She huffs and puffs and thrashes her way through the woods so you can hear her coming at a hundred yards. I walk fast for a short distance, and then I'm tired. She walks complainingly but can, if she must, keep going for many hours.

She's usually warm, whereas I feel the cold. Even in summer I often need a coat, but she casts hers off with the first signs of spring.

She drinks a great deal of coffee, and likes strong red wine. I take a small glass of spirits after dinner for my health, and only the weakest tea. I eat fish, soup, vegetables. She prefers roast meats and strong sausage and has a passion for apricots.

I sleep better than she does. When she's awake she endlessly jackknifes as if clinging to a raft that's being tossed about on a rough sea.

She loves the theatre, and I don't: I feel confined and restless, but she laughs and weeps and shouts bravo at the end so that people turn to stare.

She goes through the journals quickly and untidily, so that I have to put them back in order before I can read them.

Departures make her anxious but she loves arrivals; when she reaches her destination all her dread gives way to excitement. Away, I do exactly what I do at home. While she rushes round seeing everything, I stay in my room waiting impatiently for her return. Nor am I a sightseer at mealtimes; she eats whatever she's never eaten before.

She hates the return, finds the house uncongenial, the countryside bleak, and feels trapped and lonely. And though she rarely sits and stares out of the window, or hesitates when asked to account for her day, since she always has a pile of books to read, letters to answer, neighbours to receive, sometimes it's as if fear catches up with her: she goes to bed with mysterious symptoms, pulls the blankets up over her face, refuses all medicines and comfort until – as suddenly as she succumbs, she recovers, jumps out of bed, throws open the windows, and runs through the house as if astonished to be alive…

Those words are mine, in fact, not Charles's. Increasingly, I found myself drawn to the gaps in Belle's story, episodes that were suggested but in detail could only be guessed at; not her life so much as how I imagined the parts of it that were lost to us. Such as the matter of her childlessness: I was tempted to give her a phantom child, but there's no reason to believe she conjured one, except in the offspring, often fatherless, of protagonists in her novels.

As d'Hermenches had predicted, Belle soon became bored in the small Swiss town near Neuchâtel. She wrote little other than letters (the first great correspondence of her life was over, the second yet to begin) and gave herself over to daily life – with increasing impatience at its banalities. In one account she sits surrounded by guests but speaking to no one. Her silence and her scowling face attracted their glances but warned them to keep their distance.

The pastor said something witty. Well he might. If she could have tolerated his cynicism he might have been a friend for her.

'What did you say?' Belle called, jumping up.

'We're speaking of the joy a virtuous person brings both to himself and to those around him.'

'Only an unvirtuous person could claim such a thing.'

The pastor, naturally, was taken aback; she could see she interested him. What had he said to Charles? – that she revealed herself more than she realised.

'Virtue in the sense you mean it – sticking to a list of pointless rules with stubborn imperviousness – is an hypocrisy: it makes a misery of the person who flaunts it, and he makes misery for everyone else.'

'And you, how would you define it?'

'It's living as you want and doing the work you were born for.'

The pastor's wife raised her voice: 'There's no contradiction between virtue and misery, or rather, perhaps, happiness doesn't by definition follow from virtue, though it might.'

'My dear' – the pastor – 'you're always so moderate, a devotee of the middle way, whereas Belle and I are extremists.'

Belle didn't like this at all, either being claimed by the pastor as a kindred spirit or the snub he dealt his wife. She turned her back to them, picked up the teapot, and moved restlessly among her guests to fill their cups.

The years passed, still she wrote little – until something roused her, perhaps closure of the long and debilitating search for fertility, then the panicked realisation that she'd been waiting for her life to begin when in fact it was already half over. In desperation, she produced three short epistolary novels in a row. Championing the cause of women who in one way or another are at odds with the staid and convention-bound world they inhabit – an unhappy wife, an unmarried mother, a young girl humiliated by the search for a husband –, they incriminate the tyrannical authority of stupid, insensitive men. Every citizen of Neuchâtel saw himself pictured in her books, which brought her local fame and notoriety.

They would walk. That had already been decided, as an economy and to do themselves good. They walked in silence because otherwise they would bicker. In any case Belle, come straight from her desk, hadn't yet freed her mind of the day's writing and was rehearsing her sentences. Charles thought of a woman with a great nest of hair, its curls and ringlets like a golden haze round her long pale face. Turning a corner, they were suddenly in a crowd, and Belle felt her stomach tighten with nerves. Were all these people heading for the concert? So many she would have to greet and name one to another. She began to rehearse the names of those she knew would be there but then stopped at the futility of it.

'There was a sigh,' Charles said, not unkindly.

'Are all these people on their way to hear Ragrid?'

'Who knows who they are – does it matter? Anyway, you like to get lost in a crowd.'

'That's true.'

'But do try to be civil to anyone we know.'

'Have you ever known me not civil?' Belle turned on him so abruptly that a pin sprung from her hair, out of the knot she hadn't rearranged for the occasion. She let it go, and Charles moved ahead as if – she thought – to distance himself.

She noticed Colette, come from Lausanne, had her eye fixed on Charles's retreating back and might have been trying to catch him up until she caught sight of Belle and quickly smiled and waved. There was a muddle: as they embraced Colette's famous hair got caught in Belle's sleeve. Charles came back to disentangle them, and Colette, laughing shrilly, went careering up the steps into the village hall. Charles watched her go with a sort of flustered complacency. Suddenly, Belle understood, a spark of intuition, and with it came the searing pain of humiliation.

Charles scraped the plate with his knife, wiped the knife with the lump of bread he'd been kneading with the fingers of his left hand, and then ate the doughy result. As his fingers deposited the morsel in his mouth he looked towards the window, and didn't notice that Belle shuddered as his fleshy lips closed on the bread. Slowly he chewed it. Then he swallowed, and glanced at her as if he'd sensed her disgust and was challenging her to express it.

Unless he was simply oblivious of his actions, distracted by wariness – as he had always been wary of her brilliance, and how much more so now, with the shame – or in defiance – of having broken his marriage vows to her. He looked towards the window again as if it might offer a means of escape.

'Are you going to Lausanne?' Her voice was harsh, and made him flinch. He stared at her with surprise – or was it distaste for her crudeness? Perhaps he was simply afraid of her cutting words.

She sat back, lolled almost, and jeered: 'But I should be grateful to you.'

'Grateful?'

'For making my position so clear to me.'

'Your position is exactly what it's always been. You're my wife...'

'Exactly. And you are my husband.'

He couldn't follow her into the treacherous waters of her sarcasm. He faltered, looked away, but not, this time, towards the window.

She leant across the table. Suddenly she was intense, almost hissing the words in her haste to expel them. 'I don't blame you, you know. My own case is no less despicable.'

'I've always esteemed you. Your gifts –'

'Of course.'

'I offered you an escape.'

'From my family? Oh yes, and freed me from the unspeakable humiliation of looking for a husband. Don't mistake me, Charles. I'm grateful. You have exposed my hypocrisy. But how can I live with it?'

'Live with what? I've told you it's over.'

'Live with my error. Mine.'

An error that wouldn't have occurred if for once in her life she'd listened to the advice of others. Or probed her feelings instead of attending only to the logic of her mind which had entirely convinced her of the sense of it: marriage to the tutor.

At last their eyes met, and she found herself unable to look away. What did he see? Her customary disdain, perhaps. Or the blank incomprehension of a trapped creature before it's found the strength to flee.

Never again

A daily walk round the square. The circumnavigation. Never mind how. Shuffling would do – until, all of a sudden, I'm on the tips of my toes and breaking into a run, hurtling forwards, and clutching at the railings in an attempt to halt my mad rush.

Not to trip and fall, anything but that trickster's joke, played by my body in league with a god of slapstick. Only concentrate. The usual drill – heels to ground, a deep breath, then, balanced, let go, stand, think about walking, one foot in front of the other. DO NOT RUN.

The pretence of normality, as if passing the time of day, looking over the railings into the children's playground. Would this be easier if I was truly old? A time might come when people didn't turn their heads, I'd be invisible. But not yet. Not to the young girl staring at me from the playground, so entranced with the spectacle I made that she ignored the calls of a friend on the swings behind her.

A memory of childhood: perched in my tree (shimmering copper leaves) in the back garden of our house in Hampstead. Invisible, as I thought, to anyone on the ground. Invisible certainly to the old woman in the garden next door. Just an old woman, except that perhaps she wasn't so old, perhaps no more than sixty, or less, in any case someone to be mildly curious about only because she was afflicted in some way, referred to by adults in hushed voices, as if to speak louder was to risk contagion. The woman, old or not, had two sticks to support her, and was somehow stuck, half turning back to the house, as if she'd thought better of a walk down the garden, but could neither go back nor proceed.

Now I caught sight of a wispy figure. The apparition seemed to dog my steps. Several times now I had seen him standing in the same place on the corner of the square. Most people stared at me with curiosity – with amusement if they thought I was drunk, with fear if they were older and thought they recognised their own fate in mine. But he looked with a keen, objective interest, his eye following my progress round the square. I'd turned him into a beneficent figure, in preference to the dread I initially associated with his appearances. No longer afraid of him, I concentrated on walking forward in stately fashion, hoping he'd register my smooth progress, my wily control.

The girl still stared. Should I smile? Smile. But no, the child turned away, ran off to join her friend. And I was on my toes again, clutching, until I thought to relax my grip, just a fingertip would do it.

Still, I kept falling. My injuries were like those sustained in a school playground – chipped front tooth, grazed knee, sprained ankle – but with the additional old-age risk of a broken hip, so I began to take tablets. It was some weeks before they had an effect, but when it happened it was dramatic. I was walking with Victor on the Heath, with my usual tendency to rush forward uncontrollably, my sailor's lurch, when suddenly, from one moment to the next, from one footstep to the next, my stride lengthened, smoothed out, and I found my pace again. Victor, noticing it too, commented, and I replied, 'Don't say anything', as if my reprieve might not hold if we paid it too much attention. It lasted three hours, and then just as suddenly I lost it, but only until the next tablet kicked in. For a time I was saved.

At some point I began to be erratic in company, prone to making aggressive statements that offended people. It seemed to me that I always had a good reason for my rudeness, which usually came out of my irritation at someone's complacency. Victor said that at the best of times I was more than usually vehement, that these lightning switches of mood in me shocked people including him.

It seemed to me I was simply stating an opinion, and as far as I was concerned this was an advance on my previous inability to say anything at all unless it was to ask simple questions about someone's métier or marital status. According to Victor it was alright to be vehement about some things, things that mattered, but not about little things like the shape of a car or the colour of a wall. For me, then, everything seemed to matter. But the vehemence didn't insult people as my lapses into aggression did. These remarks were completely unexpected, they seemed to come out of some previously hidden recess of my mind, taking me by surprise as much as they did my targets. Immediately I had spoken I regretted it and would apologise and then follow up with a remorseful card. But a little later I'd feel the essential truthfulness of what I had said, if not the absolute truthfulness, then my continuing belief in the veracity of my statement, even if I still felt shame for saying it. I wondered at how, once, I had been able to coast along amicably enough with these truths about people in my head, but still I regretted speaking them because it did no good and changed nothing, especially not for me.

It seemed to me that I had crossed a border I could never traverse again, between health and sickness, autonomy and dependence, life and death. A response had to be made. I couldn't go on as I had before; rather, as I saw it, a fundamental change in my way of life was called for.

Ever again, once and for all – these were phrases often in my mind then, as if conclusiveness could be achieved, was even desirable. I felt trapped, trapped by an illness that would soon make me dependent, trapped by the man I was dependent on, trapped not least by my lack of means. I found myself imagining ways I might suddenly get a lot of money. Someone would leave me a house which I'd sell for an enormous sum – this despite the fact that I knew no one with a valuable house who might leave it to me. I imagined being kind to some shabby, lonely old man who would gratefully leave me the fortune he kept under his mattress. Then I thought of doing the lottery with a series of numbers made up of my birth date and Victor's, and though I never placed a bet, every week I'd check to see if the numbers came up.

A friend spoke of friends of his who'd bought a house by the sea in Denmark. It cost them almost nothing, this house: there was a story about a farmer's wife, or widow, who owned the house – it was on land belonging to the farm – and whose children didn't want to become farmers. And so when these friends of our friend saw the empty house, raised above the dunes, overlooking a wide empty beach and the sea, and went to the farmer's wife and asked to buy it, she agreed. Apparently there were lots of such houses because people in Denmark preferred to live in the city or leave their country altogether.

The story set me thinking. The idea of a house by the sea in Denmark – a place I'd barely ever thought of before – seemed irresistible. I imagined a wooden shack with a veranda along the front, and sitting on the veranda to watch the sun sink into the sea and, once the sun had gone and there was a chill in the air, sitting inside the shack beside an old-fashioned stove and listening to the waves breaking on the shore.

I went to the library and took out some guidebooks, and then I found out about flights to Copenhagen, and tried to make contact with the friends of our friend to learn more details. I was all set to go. Finally I got hold of them, and it turned out that our friend had got the story wrong. The house didn't overlook the sea, it was several miles inland. And it wasn't in Denmark but in Sweden – it was just that you could get to it from Denmark, crossing the causeway from one country to the other. Also, though the house was very cheap it needed many repairs, which they, being handy people, were doing themselves. As far as they knew there weren't lots of such houses, and finding theirs had been chance. All in all I had to let it go.

I asked myself what I would do if I was alone in the world, for one reason or another. Obviously I'd have to change everything. I'd have to move to a distant suburb, or another town, or the countryside. And then, though I'd have little choice but to go on with the work I did now, I would live simply. I wouldn't eat meat or drink wine, go to cafés, travel, see films, or ever spend recklessly in a shop. I'd stay at home, living modestly on the pittance I earned, with my cats for company, and reading books borrowed from the library. This, too, was a fantasy and, with its stringent, heroic aspect, by no means an unbearable one.

I also asked myself how it was that I did work that didn't guarantee my way of life, and it seemed impossible, because too late, to do any other kind of work. But then I thought that I must have had a hunch which had led me to make the choices I had, mainly the choice to write, and that if I were faithful to that hunch and waited long enough, it would bear fruit or at least a ray of light would fall on my situation and then I would understand it and know what to do and perhaps even have the power to do it. I kept thinking of that ray of light, about what it meant, which was partly elucidation. But perhaps it was also the spotlight into which I would walk to collect my unearned prize. It was my lucky moment.

It came, my ray of light, one early morning with a call from my godfather Lomas.

When I'd said goodbye to him, I went to tell Victor what was proposed. He was in the bath, rinsing shampoo out of his hair. I sat on the lavatory lid and waited till he'd finished.

'That was Lomas.'

'Oh?'

'He's offering us the Orkney house for the winter.'

'What do you mean?'

'What I say. He wants someone there because last winter it became infested with rats. He's away for three months, from January to March. Long enough for us to settle in and get some work done, with nothing to distract us.'

Victor hoisted himself out of the bath and when he quickly grabbed a towel to hide his nakedness I knew he was upset with me.

He was unyielding: 'It's out of the question,' he said before I'd even finished my explanation. 'I'm committed to things here. Anyway how would we live?'

'I'll go on editing as I do here. Publishers post work out, and it doesn't make any difference whether they send it to the next street or to the other end of the country.'

'Well, you've obviously made up your mind.'

He left the bathroom, and I followed him. 'I haven't made up my mind. I hoped we could discuss it.'

'I can't go. It's very simple. If you want to, then you'd better do it, though it'll be the first time we've gone our separate ways.'

'No, it won't. What about America – you were away for two months.'

'I see, this is a revenge, is it?' He was pulling shirts out of a drawer as if he couldn't find the one he wanted. I stood at the door of the bedroom, afraid of his anger, and of my own resolution.

'Of course it's not. The circumstances are completely different.'

'Why bring it up then?'

'Because you said – oh come on, I was questioning your histrionic suggestion that I'm walking out on you.'

'Well, aren't you?'

'I want you to come too.'

'So you've decided to go, come what may. This is hardly a discussion.'

'You're just turning the tables on me, misrepresenting everything I say.'

He was pulling a shirt over his head, and his next words were muffled. '... what you have to do.'

'What?'

'You must do what you have to do. But know that I can't join you.'

'Well then, I won't go.' And I left the room.

Later, he came to find me at my desk. He stood behind me and I didn't turn round.

'Look, I can't go. I can't and I don't want to. And I won't pretend I'm happy about your going alone. Can you cope on your own? But you must do what you want – always.'

I became ill, ordinarily ill, like anyone might, with flu. I lay on the bed and stared out of the window at a brick wall. I picked up the book at my side and read a few lines wherever it fell open. Or closed my eyes in hope of sleep – and daydreamed of the wondrous house I'd given Belle...

I came to with a start. Victor was sitting at the end of the bed. He heard my description of Belle's rural paradise and proceeded to denounce nature and solitude as poison.

'We'd be mad,' he said, 'to flee our lives in London, to imagine we could sustain an existence in an alien countryside. I can't drive and you soon won't be able to – you have to have a car in the country. Nor are we handy. And you can't even encounter a cow without going into a blue funk. Anyway, Belle wanted only to get away from the country and get to Paris.'

'It's not as simple as that. She wanted to get away from her husband.'

'I see.'

'But that's not what I want.'

'No?'

'No.'

'What do you want then? I suppose this is all a part of the adjustment to your illness. In a year's time you'll see it for what it is.'

'Oh? What's that?'

'Flights of fancy.' He jumped up and began to stride round the room. He stood at the window but not as if he was looking at anything, rather as if he was composing his next sentences in his head. Then he turned towards me and said between gritted teeth, 'You've become so discontented. You never used to be like this. It's as if nothing can make you happy.'

At a loss for words of explanation, I turned away from his own desperation, his sense of entrapment – did I even see them? – and burying my face in the pillow, sought oblivion in Belle's great escape.

Neither moon nor stars lit the rolling hills around the house. Belle, sleepless, sat up and traced a faint looming where black sky met a blacker earth. An irrelevancy preoccupied her: that she hadn't recognised the signs. And this despite having imagined his infidelity so often, as if it would have released her from her own obligations. They had been calm in those months. She was busy with her writing and Charles rarely impinged on her thoughts. It had seemed to her, fleetingly one evening, that at last they'd found a way of coexisting peaceably.

Ruth, her friend and helper, found her in yesterday's clothes when she brought in the morning coffee – as if the nightly ritual of sleep had escaped her notice. When she drew her attention to her crumpled dress Belle seemed baffled. But she went meekly to the basin, stood passively while Ruth poured water, handed soap and towels, gently helped her get out of her clothes. And then, as if her will suddenly asserted itself, Belle went at the job of washing with immense, excessive zeal.

Perhaps it was Ruth who arranged her getaway, for Belle was incapable of it – and it was against her principles to leave a marriage. Unless Charles himself understood the necessity – her need to distance herself, his own to consider his position, the impossibility of continuing as they were – and set about making the arrangements. And paying for them, for he possessed what she had brought to the marriage and perhaps, in his chagrin, was more than ready to finance her escape. A ticket for the journey to Paris, somewhere for her to stay, money to live on. Belle didn't have to spell out the terms. Charles, that most practical of men, bought his way out of trouble.

Who knows who might have seen her? – seen and taken note, of a woman dressed in a pale-coloured costume, an eau de nil, not the most sensible of colours for travelling. A certain disarray marked her – the garment had once been stylish but had now lost its crisp line and hung a little baggily on her. It was as if for many weeks her looks had been the last thing on her mind. Her hair was harshly and thoughtlessly pulled back from her face which was blotched with red. Since she was of an age when women for the most part went unnoticed, perhaps her fellow travellers didn't see her agitation. Her lips moved in silent conversation with herself or some absent other, and her hands twisted a handkerchief for something to do. But then, it was as if she decided: enough, life goes on, mine no less than anyone else's – and with a determined air she opened her bag and took out a book, opened the book, and appeared to read.

In the days that followed, whenever the coach stopped she looked up. Her hand tightened its grasp on the book, anxiety tensed her forehead. Did she expect to be dragged off, prevented from reaching her destination? Only when the coach set off again did she sink back into the seat, and close her eyes for a moment before going back to her book. But then – on the last leg of the journey, when streets and houses replaced fields beyond the window – she peered out and held herself tightly as if to quell her excitement.

She struggled through the crowd towards the Rivettes – two smiling faces bobbing up between backs of heads only to disappear again. They greeted her with hugs. Paul took her case, Agnes her arm. There was no call for her to speak since they answered their questions for her: What a crowd! Has her journey been a trial? – How pale she looks, and hungry, but they've made a lamb stew ... a glass of wine; is she really to stay a year? They've found her an apartment, a steep climb up but lots of sky to make her feel at home; what's she reading? – she looked down at the book she still clutched in her hand and couldn't remember, but Paul lifted her arm and proclaimed 'Pascal', to which Agnes, astonished, cried, 'On a coach!'

Then, in the carriage, one on each side of her, they calmed down. Agnes was still holding her arm and Paul now gently took her hand. Faltering, her voice pitched high from strain, at last Belle managed to speak. 'I – have – taken – a – great – step.'

Benjamin

A long climb up past imposing doors, coming at last to one so small it might have been a cupboard. They all stood panting as Paul managed the key. Then the tentative entry into an eyrie – so high, so safe – and the flood of sunlight on that particular morning, streaming into every room like the light of heaven.

'We were worried about the view, that you can't see the street. We'd want to.'

But she preferred not to know there was a street. Streets frightened her to begin with, she couldn't find her pace and people seemed to stare.

'It's very small – the rooms are small – but at least there are several.'

And each one off a corridor. She liked the corridor, for walking up and down.

'You could work at the kitchen table. There's no one to disturb you.'

She especially liked the kitchen, its big sky.

How many ways of describing a sky. How many different skies to describe. Usually from the point of view of a building, as if a sky needed a foil, as a landscape did.

A great copper dome in the distance that would catch an early morning sun, so dazzling she'd have to look away. Yes, in that wet spring she was able to describe to her friends a dawn sky that was transparent blue.

In a drizzle the dome would turn green against a low grey sky. When the sky turned bilious it hardly showed.

And not only the dome, but a church tower, and the river a silver slick to one side visible if she pressed her face against the window, and endless series of roofs, some with figures on them – a woman hanging up washing, a man tending his pigeons, children with a kite.

She turned away from the view and laughed. The anxious-looking faces of Paul and Agnes broadened into relieved smiles. It was decided.

Solitude – she wondered that she'd had to endure a marriage to achieve it. She wanted only to stay in her attic and walk from room to room, arrange her books, and stand at the window and look at the view.

Once she had settled, her greatest pleasure was to go into a café, sit down, order a coffee, and open a book. Opening the book was the point. Not reading it or drinking the coffee, but having ordered the coffee, opening the book in preparation for reading it once she'd drunk the coffee. What was it about this act? The freedom of reading – not that Charles wasn't a reader as she was, not that she hadn't always made her own rules. But to open a book in the midst of a crowd who took not the slightest notice of her and know that she might read undisturbed with only the deadline of the café's closing time – this was joy.

Charles would acquire a posthumous reputation in his ancestral village: was said to have fathered at least one child there. But it's often claimed that it was Belle's affair, with a younger man, that rocked their marriage, bringing about her removal to Paris. It seems unlikely from what we know of her principles; also the pattern of her relationships. What she was best at was passionate friendship conducted mostly by letter –

what she had had with d'Hermenches would now, by an odd chance, be mirrored by his young nephew.

As Benjamin would describe their meeting, at a salon in Paris, as soon as he set eyes on her, he understood her significance for him. She stood apart, silently watching, with that look on her face he would come to know well, which was partly disdain but also an acute awareness. Then, when she spoke, she expressed herself with originality and liveliness, with a contempt for conventional opinion that was exactly what people noted – and criticised – in him.

For Belle, it was nothing like that. There was little in his appearance that could possibly draw her – wasn't one young man much like another? Only the fact of his being the nephew of d'Hermenches marked him out. And that he had read her novels, had something to say about them.

They talked, that first time, about freedom, mainly Benjamin's lack of it. His father, the most controlling of men, it seemed to Belle, demanded that his son return home to the job that had been set up for him – when nothing was so obnoxious to Benjamin as the feeling that his freedom and independence of movement were endangered.

'So, what do you want to do?' she asked.

'Go to England and roam about.'

'Ah! An escapade, a vagabond's life in the land of the free. Excellent!'

Flight had been Belle's solution, and she was keen to encourage others to follow her example. Never mind that she would return to Charles, and that Benjamin would eventually fall in with his father's plans for him.

Meanwhile, they were rarely seen except together.

They attended meetings, readings, parties, and they talked in transit, on their way from one event to the next. As they talked, they explored the city, and with each new street or building discovered, one or other expressed yet another opinion that had them exclaiming at their affinity.

Others would see her steal a glance at her young friend, a look of intense, and private, excitement. Who knows what she hoped for? In any case it didn't really figure, since Benjamin sought only affirmation, and glowed in the warmth of her understanding.

As he saw it in those early weeks of friendship in Paris, she helped him find his gift: 'I have given up the idea of a novel,' he would write to her from England. 'I am too talkative by nature. All those people wanting to speak for me. I like to speak for myself, above all so that you can hear me.'

It's unlikely he misled her. He told her about a mad plan to marry for money so as to clear the debts that made him dependent on his father's goodwill. She looked askance, laughing harshly as if at a bad joke. And then said something about people who have no thoughts for anything but their own ups and downs – delivered with a searching glance that he shiftily evaded, launching into an account of what he planned to do in England.

It was Charles who paid for his passage across the Channel. A year after Belle's arrival in Paris, he had written to suggest he might join her, since he too felt stale and in need of the stimulus of a city for a time – as if it was understood between them that their separation was only a temporary expedient, and sooner or later she would return.

She found him at her door one afternoon, patiently

waiting. She came along the street and saw a thin figure leaning against a tree and reading a newspaper. At first she took it to be Paul, and quickened her pace. But then, oddly, when she realised her mistake, rather than feeling disappointed, or even appalled, she was touched. He looked vulnerable, a countryman overwhelmed by the mayhem of the city, using his paper as a defence against the curious glances of passers-by. Clearly he had come to fetch her home.

Perhaps she had always known that her sense of loyalty would permit no other ending. Also, she admitted to feeling uneasy at the centre of things, preferring always a life on the margins. She was too outspoken, too impatient of etiquette to tolerate Parisian hypocrisies, which couldn't accommodate her uncompromising truthfulness.

Perhaps Benjamin made it possible – and necessary – for her to return. Their friendship would make it bearable – and the presence in her life of a tolerant husband would allow her complete freedom.

'You don't mind?' Belle feared he'd regard her request for Benjamin's fare as outrageous.

'Haven't I always accepted your friends? I'm glad to help a young man on his way, though I don't think his father will thank us for it.'

'They'll have to be reconciled eventually.'

'But for the time being an adventure will do the boy no harm.'

Belle was perhaps too taken up with her young friend to see that Charles might have another motive. If he was jealous he didn't show it, but perhaps he saw how it was for her, and for her own sake as much as his own wanted Benjamin's removal.

Tourism

I descended into a house that was not, as I had feared, dark and chill, for Victor had stoked the stove before leaving and switched on the table lights so that eddies of warmth greeted me. I felt the loss of him keenly, as a dull ache in my side, and wondered at his goodness in bringing me to that place.

I sat at the kitchen table with a cup of tea. Slowly the dim light of morning gave form to what lay outside: the field in front of the house, the road, the lake beyond, and finally the sea, a strip of dark grey beneath a low, bruised sky. I watched the sheep in the field, and some swans flying over the lake, and a bus rounding the lake to stop at a farm on the far side. Suddenly, my view was blocked by a creature on the window-sill, my companion, the cat Iso. I got up and opened the window, which the wind almost wrenched out of my hand, and Iso came in, yowling for food.

In several more layers of clothes, I took the track down to the sea, and the wind came at me, so that every step was an effort and I thought only of putting one foot in front of the other. When at last I reached the water I looked for the seals that had appeared for Victor, as he said they would for me, curious to watch and stare.

I called out, as he had done, doubting that my voice, cracked by self-consciousness, could reach the seals above the sounds of wind and water. But then they appeared, smooth black heads bobbing about on the waves, and sniffing the air as if they heard or saw with their snouts. I counted six of them before turning away to walk back to the house, the wind behind me now, carrying me along as if I was sailing.

Later, I set out for the shop. The road rose steeply upwards. Land, sea, air alike were spacious, but not the houses, which huddled here and there, low and ugly, into dips in the hill, as if seeking shelter from the hurtling gales. By the time I reached the crest of the hill I felt hot and unbuttoned my coat which then flew behind me, almost torn off my arms by the wind, so that I had to turn round and with my back to the wind do it up again. Then I took off my hat, but my loosened hair blew across my face and blinded me.

A crowd of people filled the shop. They gave no sign of noticing me until my turn came and then they stopped their talk to hear me declare myself. I asked for the items I wanted – 'Not too many,' I said, in the way of conversation, 'so I can carry them.'

'Where have you got to carry them to?'

'To Lomas's, I'm looking after Lomas's place. You must be Marie – Lomas mentioned you.'

'How are you managing?'

'So far so good' – and I laughed, too loudly, and when Marie echoed my laugh she also sounded false, and quickly asked: 'Doesn't Lomas have a car?'

'It's broken down,' I said, 'and since it doesn't have a licence, as Lomas explained it, I thought I wouldn't bother with it, I'll walk, it's good for me.'

'Aye,' said Marie, 'if you've got the strength.'

And a woman standing near said, 'Billy Kidd will fix it, and no one bothers with licences, do they?' – looking round at the company and someone laughed.

Marie said, 'Aye, Billy Kidd,' and gave me his number.

Walking back with the bags of groceries, which were almost more than I could carry though they would last me only a few days, I stopped at the phone box to ring this Billy Kidd. He heard me out and said he'd come over, but not that day, and if not the next then the one after.

I didn't like to leave the house in case he came. I kept an eye on the road because I couldn't hear anything above the soughing wind, not a car come up the track, nor a caller shouting, and though I thought Billy Kidd was likely just to walk in and keep on going until he found me, since what else could people do in the circumstances, I couldn't risk missing him.

He didn't come that day, or the next. And not till the afternoon of the day he'd set as his deadline did I dare stray further than the yard, and then walked up the hill behind the house where I could keep the road in sight. The sun showed itself for the first time since my arrival, and sky and sea became a blue so intense that it was like the south, and not the south I'd come from, but further still: Amalfi perhaps. Except for the sodden green land and the treelessness, and above all the wind so I stood long enough only to watch a boat make its way choppily across my view until it disappeared round a headland. But still no Billy Kidd.

He came at last when my back was turned, and got on with the job. I went out to feed the geese and found the barn door open and a man with his head under the bonnet of the car. 'Shouldn't let it waste,' he said in greeting, as if I was resisting the idea of driving the car.

He joined me after for a dram, and we talked of the stove. Every morning I woke to find it fading, and before anything else could be done it had to be brought back to life, and then every minute fussed over, my only source of warmth and hot water and cooked food.

'These days people have electric cookers and heaters. They may still have their stoves but not to depend on.'

'Lomas hasn't got round to it yet,' I said. 'For years he's been only a summer visitor.'

'Aye,' said Billy Kidd, 'ayee. Summers are easy, it's the winters you have to look out for.'

I'd read about the Viking bands that had holed up there and drank themselves numb through days that were mostly nights. Nothing much had changed, it seemed. Winter consisted of waiting for spring as best you could.

Daily I walked down to the sea, either the nearby sea, the view from the house, where I sang to the seals; or the sea beyond the headland, where I stood on slabs of slate jutting out over heaving planes of water and looked towards even more northerly places – Iceland, or Norway. I watched it sucked into steaming eddies between the rocks, and then pulled back into the depths, a clatter of stones in pursuit. From a distance it sounded like a train, and there, at the edge, the roar deafened. Far out, in the curve of infinity, silence beckoned.

I seemed always to be watching, looking at what lay before me, and was blind when I tried to look inwards. I did the editorial work that was my living, but when I turned to Belle – to Benjamin's first, ecstatic visit to her at home – my concentration failed me. Instead, I tried writing of the view from the windows, but other people's words came out, as if it was impossible to write of landscape except in the words of literature, which were words of exalted feeling, of awe, when for me the landscape evoked unease even if sometimes, when the sun came out, and the colour, it could also astound me.

More often, as I stared out of the window, I was bored by what I saw, so that when a car crossed the scene it was immediately more interesting, for the car contained a person and I could think about who that person might be and where they were going and why.

I sought the familiarity of Lomas, in the signs of him about the place, which were partly in its bareness, the absence of much thought in its arrangements, for he hardly noticed his surroundings and gave no time to making a home, though there were odd touches of comfort, like the daybed by the fire, where he lay to read by an excellent lamp; and partly in objects, such as the shelf of treasures, mementoes of his years in Africa, each one specially chosen or received, a stone, a shell, a carved wooden deity; or the row of his shoes and boots by the back door, battered but clean, and dependable in their upright orderliness.

I lived a life of extreme regularity, dictated by the timing of the medication I took. In one sense the pills, having to remember to take them, exerted a tyranny that never allowed me to forget I was sick, but mainly, as tools of control, they liberated me. So long as I remembered to take them at exactly the right time, for much of the day I was fit and active – and if I forgot or they failed to kick in I just sat at home until they took effect. I was never required to be anywhere or to see anyone and could easily enough accommodate the fluctuations in my condition.

Standing at the sink one early morning as the kettle

slowly filled, I looked out into the retreating darkness and listened to the radio news. It was the same news I would have heard in the south, spoken in a familiar voice, though I heard it in a place so far from home, so remote from anything I knew, that for a moment I didn't know where I was, I felt in both places, split, or in neither place. Then my mind went blank and I couldn't recall anything, as if the different bits of me had atomised, and all I was aware of was my hand on the tap, as if it clutched at stability while the rest of me threatened to disintegrate. And then the sodden green of the field emerged before me, and the milky lake, and the grey band of the sea separating from the low, swollen sky, and I saw too that the kettle had filled and water dripped down its sides, and Iso was on the window-sill, and the newly replenished stove crackled, and the newsreader spoke of traffic jams on a motorway into London, and then I came back together again and continued the motions of morning.

I visited an ancient burial place, a cairn protected by a large prefabricated shed: rows of tombs, each with its stone bunk where a corpse would have lain. A raised walkway traversed the length of the chamber, with creaking wooden slats and a metal handrail rusty and yet damp to the grasp. A musty-smelling place suggesting bats in its girdered heights and rats in its shadowed depths, but what undermined me was not only these associated horrors but the sense of enclosure, of entrapment, for the door had clicked shut behind me. Fear tightened its grip on me and all I could think of was getting out, or not being able to, and I started to run, the walkway shuddering with my heavy footfall. I jumped down the steps and tried to force the door which at first wouldn't open because of my hamfistedness. When at last I got it open I fled.

I headed for the promontory, stumbling on tufts and clouts and then on a heap of matted wool that was firm against my foot: a sheep, and dead.

I picked myself up and veered off inland as the day turned dark and troubled, clouds banking blackly over the brae. I ran against the wind which seemed to want to force me back towards the cairn and the dead sheep. But then my walking began to fail, and I was limping and then dragging my feet, and feeling drained and exhausted, but none the less got back to the house where I collapsed on to the couch in the living room.

I watched a hearse go by on the road: a long black hatchback. As it crossed my view it seemed to become a ghostly progression in the murky afternoon light. I watched it turn off the road and come up the track towards the house, and as it got closer it seemed first to get blacker and then to fade into the dingy surrounds, and when I went out to greet the driver I saw that it wasn't a hearse but an ordinary, featureless van, and not black but green. The driver was delivering something for Lomas, some shelves he'd ordered from a carpenter.

Later, when the man had gone, and I sat at the kitchen table with a purring Iso on my lap and drank tea, I asked myself why I had mistaken a van for a hearse. I decided it was partly the poor light, but that alone wasn't enough to explain my error. There was something else as well. It was as if an archetype of death had taken hold of me.

Things began to break and fail. First, a piece fell off the stove, a brick positioned just inside the door, which broke up as it fell inwards into the flames. I worried that it mattered, that brick, and such little worries began to fill my life, taking the place of big worries, though they threatened, these little worries, to coalesce into a larger one.

Snow came, a scattering of powder, striping the brown-green hills with white. I found on Lomas's shelves a volume of tales of the old Icelanders who, six centuries before me, listened to the telling of what I in my solitude read in a book. It occurred to me that, just like the islanders, these stories ignored the landscape and the weather. The remarkable day, for them, was the day when the wind didn't blow too much, and there wasn't ice or snow or mud, and no one got cold or wet, which happened rarely, and so the landscape and the elements were just a backcloth to be forgotten, when for me they ruled everything and once I had taken them into account there was no escaping them.

When water ceased to flow from the taps, Marie at the shop said it was an island problem, the silting up of water pipes, and that a compressor would fix it. The people to go to for a compressor were the Robertsons at the farm across the lake: Alan – who appeared when I knocked, looked bleary-eyed at me, and stumbling turned away – and Shona – who came in his place, looked askance as she heard my story, and didn't ask me in out of the wind and rain. She agreed, though, to lend the machine.

First, clumsily, I unscrewed the pipe to the mains at the back of the house, as Shona had described it, but then couldn't fix the compressor to the pipe, and even if I had been able to, I feared turning on the electrics that would galvanise it, because if it worked the water would gush out and perhaps I'd not be able to stop it, by screwing up the pipes again, and the puddle at my feet would fast become a lake, what with the rain and the rivulets too that splashed down the hillside.

Meanwhile a trickle of water found its way past the scarf round my neck and I felt the icy trail down my back. I cursed the Robertsons, and I cursed Lomas, and even Victor, and then I cursed myself for the hubris that had deluded me into believing I could survive in such a place, let alone handle a compressor. And then, finally, I went in to call Marie, not knowing who else to turn to, and heard the catch in my voice, the threatening tears, which Marie would hear too, and sent her husband, who'd just come in and still wore his outdoor clothes.

So Marie's Tony fixed it and accepted my jabbering thanks, but wouldn't come in for a dram, being so wet, and then it was as if the worst had happened and I had lived to tell the tale, which was how I put it in a letter to Victor, composed in my head as I lay in a hot bath and thought how I'd open some wine. Later the cat Iso got into the mood of things and after gobbling my dinner scraps sat on the kitchen table and gazed at me as I thought of what I had left behind in London, of Victor, whom I'd so recklessly abandoned, our flat, and life together, and then of what had brought me there, the restlessness that came with the illness, the impossibility of going on as before. It never occurred to me that I might not return, nor did I doubt that Victor would have me, but still I carried with me a sense of distance between us. The unquestioning love and admiration that I had felt for him, and believed he had felt for me, had been undermined by our responses to my illness. I had been dismayed by his failure, as I saw it, to understand my needs; and he, no less so, by my sudden dependency, and its frightening implications for his future which my demands seemed to encapsulate. And though the crack might be repaired, had to some extent been so by his accompanying me to the island, it had happened and I feared would leave its permanent scar of distrust. But then I imagined Victor visiting me, so that it seemed for a while, in my cups, as if I was waiting for the letter that would announce his arrival and even for his arrival itself.

I wrote to him regularly, short notes that spoke straightforwardly of my days. He sent me cards, with similarly conventional messages – but I knew that for Victor it was all in the image and to this I always paid attention.

About half way through my stay, he sent a picture of a sculpture by Brancusi: a block of stone carved with two pairs of embracing arms, and four eyes, and two mouths squashed sideways because their faces were pressed so tightly together. Hair – undulating lines – flowed down the back of the woman and was cropped on the scalp of the man.

This was followed, a couple of weeks later by an Egyptian pair statue – a husband and wife standing side by side, her arm tight round his waist, and his round her neck, a hand flat on her breast, strong and upright like comrades.

To break my isolation I attended a musical evening at a bar on the other side of the island. It was no more than half full when I arrived, and not seeing a place at one of the tables where people already sat, and in any case worrying that it might seem presumptuous to sit with people I didn't know, I took a place at an empty table, where no one else sat down until all the other seats were taken, and the last guests, who turned out to be Shona and Alan Robertson, had no alternative but to join me.

Her mother, who accompanied them, carried the day. The old woman was deaf like so many people on the island, presumably because of the wind, and couldn't hear a single word that was said to her. That didn't stop her talking a great deal herself which, in view of her son's moroseness and Shona's and my effortfulness, was to be welcomed. Alan broke his silence only once, to ask, quite out of the blue, if I knew what an FEB was. Fucking English Bastard, he said, and threw back his head with a mad, braying laugh. And so it was until the fiddle started up and we three women sat back to listen while Alan stolidly drank his way though many drams.

A man called John, who Marie put me on to when the barn door blew in one night in a gale, and who came every day for a week to mend it – John told me many things. He spoke of the quarrels between island families, who carried their feuds from one generation to the next, that Marie and Tony for example were at the throats of the family that owned the bar, and that their feud, whose origins lay deep in the past, now played itself out on the local council. He said that Alan Robertson was sometimes found drunk in a ditch, and this was Shona's cross which she bore resentfully.

And he explained that there were two ways to live on the island, and one was to get involved, and the other was not to, but that if you were an incomer you were judged meddling if you chose the first, and snooty if the second. So while he, John, as an islander, could be remote, a bit of a recluse, which he was, I as an incomer could not be – not that anyone would like me more for not being, and not that it applied in my case anyway because I was just a visitor and people thought of me, if they thought of me at all, as a tourist.

At last the day came when I walked out and was able to unbutton my coat without the wind's wrenching it off me. The first spring day, and I walked over the hill at the back of the house to the ruins of an old church. I poked about the graves and read the inscriptions and imagined those dead men and women, especially the young ones. It was as if, I thought, I was burying something – grief for my illness, perhaps, and all its attendant distortions, even the disease itself – and I felt taken out of myself, almost in ecstasy, or delusion, which came from the blueness of the sea all around and the greenness of the turf and the playfulness of the birds and the softness of the air, and it was as if everything that had happened to me had been leading up to this moment, which was the point of it all – and this feeling stayed with me after I had returned to the house and with Iso watched from the window as night fell.

When the car failed, finally, I didn't phone Billy Kidd but decided to rely on my own two feet. At the shop Marie was all concern but saw the sense of it – put it away and forget about it, one less worry. That day Marie's Tony was driving my way and gave me a lift with the shopping; another, Shona Robertson passed near the crest of the hill and stopped to pick me up. Now that my time was almost over it was as if she remembered herself, put herself out, and agreed to come in for tea. She sat at the kitchen table and told of her son in Australia, so that I felt her poignancy, her

73

sense of being stranded on the island, and her longing for her grandchildren; and her silence about her husband was more moving than complaints, of which she must have had many.

As she got up to leave she thought to ask whether I had been lonely on the island so far from home, and I said that yes, I had, but that was what I had come for, to be lonely, to see where it got me, and Shona replied that she could understand that, that loneliness wasn't the worst thing so long as you were on your own, though if you weren't it might be. And went on her way as if it was something to have said it.

As my departure approached, my imagination, ahead of me, let go of the place: it no longer assaulted me and confined me in the present, but left my mind free to roam. I thought about how it would be to walk unimpeded by mud and wind and layers of clothes, in fact not to have to walk at all but to catch a bus to go somewhere. And to see faces that were pale rather than raw-red, and sharp and tense rather than round and open. And to enter a shop without turning heads and to give as good as I got.

I thought about Belle, the writing I might have done on the island, but hadn't, the writing I planned to do now.

Above all, I thought of Victor – and my only backward glance was at Iso, who seemed to sense I was leaving and disappeared on the morning of my last day as if to save us both from the sadness of parting.

The pink house

He had written that he would walk from the coach stop, but now it occurred to Belle that he might ignore her precise directions and cut across the fields to the house. She turned at the thought, stumbling slightly in her haste, as if she expected him to appear from the opposite direction, stealing up on her from behind to take her by surprise.

Confused, she considered the awkwardness of her position, waiting for the speck on the road that would announce him and rushing down the hill like an eager young lover (she blushed). Probably she'd fall, or twist her ankle, and in any case present the most ungainly sight, a woman with the thick figure of middle age, cantering down the track, landing at his feet out of breath (since she spent most of her life at a desk) so that she couldn't greet him but only puff in his face. Or she could wait where she was, subjecting him to the embarrassment of being watched as as he climbed the hill.

She looked down at the house – a particular view that had been her first sight of it when she returned. She'd come over the brow of the hill and seen it and something in her had responded, a moment of recognition. Oh these guarded acceptances. Why couldn't she acknowledge that as a matter of fact she loved the house? – that in her first sighting of it in the evening shadows she forgot her sense of resignation and actually felt her heart leap.

Not that the house had been part of her calculation, so far as she knew. She had rarely thought of it in the year and a half of her absence. She certainly hadn't missed it, nor had it figured in her decision to return. It was Benjamin, their intimacy and its limits, that had made it both possible and necessary for her to return. But now, as she took in the trails of smoke along the valley, the bare branches of the huge old tree behind the house, the glimmer of water beyond the wood, she believed she was right to come back, or rather, since she had no choice but to come, that in the place itself she might find fulfilment.

She was about to walk back to the house to await him more conventionally (and the cold was taking hold of her) when he appeared, not as a speck on the horizon but already halfway up the hill and calling her name.

She ran towards him, slithering on the slippery surface of the road, but without falling. Laughing, they met, and he took her hands and swung her round and round until she begged him to stop.

Then he began to talk, gabbling some story about his journey she couldn't get the point of, and then about his father – always his father –, which she listened to, as she had before, gently inclining her head as if to follow his words with the utmost attention, ready to give him the benefit of the doubt.

'A pink house!' – for some reason this was a surprise to Benjamin. She led him to her room at the back of the house, and for a moment he was shy, as if the intimacy of the room, with the desk, and her books and papers, made him aware for the first time in their short friendship that she had her own life, a writer's life and a wife's, and that though he had spoken of everything to her, she had been more cautious. 'They all blame you for my flight,' he told her.

'Ah, the malicious influence of a woman old enough to be your mother.'

'That's it. Poor creature, motherless from birth and now the plaything of an authoress.'

When Ruth came to remove the tea things she tightened her mouth so as not to laugh – at the visitor, the tall, skinny, red-haired young man who was charging back and forth, and Belle, who had that look of triumph on her face as when she'd outsmarted, without their realising it, one of the dullard neighbours. But Benjamin was equal to her cutting wit, they egged each other on – Ruth could see that at a glance as she backed out of the door with the tray. Rarely had she known Belle so animated, her cool eyes aflame.

At dinner they calmed down (no one could have kept it up in front of stolid Charles). The men behaved faultlessly to each other. Charles was responsive by his usual standards to Benjamin's literary overtures and their guest was unusually respectful of his host's remarks which he must surely – it seemed obvious to Belle – find mundane. She almost relaxed, but then Charles lost his way in an account of local politics, and she – she couldn't stop herself – snubbed him. Benjamin looked studiously away – from floundering Charles and defiant Belle – and then, to fill the silence, told a story about the dog that had been his companion in England.

Benjamin, the great talker, recorded one enduring memory of that visit to Belle. She writes at her desk, he stretches out on the couch reading. A memory of silence apart from the scratch of her pen, the turning of his pages, a memory of words but not spoken. A comfort for him, who had never before known the companionship of a like mind, let alone a home where nothing was required of him but to be himself.

'I never finish with anybody.' Benjamin spoke into the silence – about something, she assumed, he was reading. She felt a chill at his words, as if he was warning her: it can't go on for ever, one day I'll move on to greater things, but don't think I'll ever let you go entirely.

Ellénore

She lay wrapped in blankets over her day clothes because a nightdress made her feel exposed and defenceless. She traced the willow pattern of the torn wallpaper, the flood cracks in the ceiling, and a bare branch which was all she could see out of the window. Sometimes she picked up one of the books that Adolphe had placed at her side. Or closed her eyes in hope of sleep. When she knew he was out, she got off the bed and shuffled through the house to the kitchen to make a hot drink for her swollen, aching throat.

Every so often he would appear and sit at the end of the bed and tell her how desperately he wanted to leave her. He said he felt guilty about her husband, and about his father who judged him, and fearful for his job. He said that their love was doomed because it could only flourish in isolation, opposed to the world they had known until then, and such an opposition, and such a love, were untenable. They must have been mad, he said, to flee their lives, to imagine they could sustain an existence in an alien countryside. He blamed himself more than he blamed her, but while he knew he should leave her, for his sake and hers, he was incapable of doing so.

He came in windswept from long walks through the winter landscape, but he never spoke of what he saw on those walks, of whom he met. He never described the farm where he bought their meagre supplies, or the inn where he picked up his mail, letters sent in reply to his desperate messages – to his employers, his father, and, for all she knew, her husband.

Endlessly he rehearsed their affair. Certain phrases haunted him – *folie d'amour*, *l'instant fatal*, *un poids énorme* – as if he was locked in the moment when, shocked and exhausted and breathless from their flight, they had arrived at the house and she had collapsed in a fever, and all he could think of was what madness had brought them there.

And perhaps because her fever made her slow it was many days before she could write some words on a scrap of paper. Next time he came to her she handed it to him. 'What strange pity makes you afraid to break a tie which has become such a burden to you?' He stared at it wide-eyed before writing his reply, as if he too at last was speechless: 'Why don't you leave me?'

Again it was several days before she could write her answer – 'I would have left you if I'd had the strength.'

And so the days, weeks even, passed. She continued to be ill and unable to speak, but as she lay there, her throat throbbing, and he said what he'd already said many times, a phrase came into her head and repeated itself: Must I die? Must I die? Must I die? And it occurred to her that there was only one possible end to his version of their story, and that end could only be her end – she must be written off. She would have liked to protest, to reach for pen and paper and write her dissent, but something in his voice, something so apparently rational, so beguiling and insistent, stopped her. And then she found she had moved her lips, whispering it – must I die? And perhaps because it was the first time she had spoken, he noticed, and asked her to say it again, and so, making a great effort, she croaked – *faut-il que je meure?* He stared at her and paled, and grinned crookedly to mask his shame – and from that moment on she began to recover.

On-and-on-ness

Victor's snores wake me, but not irrevocably. I sink back into sleep, and follow him into a wood. It feels forbidden, so we walk carefully, delicately, over mushy wet leaves. We come almost at once to a glade of brownish reddish mulch. At first I see nothing unusual, only a slight bulging of the leaves, so that the eye is drawn to and slowly, very slowly, makes out what remains of a human being. Except that nothing remains, it's a carcass, stripped now of anything an animal might find edible, reduced to gristly skin and bones amidst the mulch. Then I see that there's another – this one all ghastly vacant eye sockets beneath a frizz of white hair. Its trunk seems to peter out where its stomach might have been, except for a femur that lies in the leaves. I get no more than a glimpse, because Victor turns back to me and takes my hand to lead me, or to be led, away.

'No one has found them yet,' he says.

'We have,' I object.

'And now someone else will too. It happens like that'

I wake with a sense of inevitability, a calm understanding that the bodies are Victor's and mine, and that is to be expected, but then I fall into a troubled half-sleep. Now I'm trying to put great blocks of text into order. It's almost tangible, this attempt, this effort, as if it isn't just in my head, thinking, but I'm actually lifting and pushing and shoving, and the blocks are slabs of concrete. I get them into order and then realise I've left one out, and I can't identify which one it is, so I start again with the ordering, and then before I reach the end I forget how it started and have to begin all over again. All I want is to sleep and forget the task, but I can't. So I get up.

If I give my brain a task to distract it, sometimes I can sneakily do what it doesn't want me to. So I stretch out the left hand as if to switch on the bedside lamp but don't – so as not to wake Victor. Then, while my brain thinks about what the left hand is up to, I coax the right foot up the bed so that the knee rises, and with the right hand grasp it and haul. It works if the foot stays flat on the bed, but tonight it won't, when I pull on my knee it jerks up towards my forehead and before I know it I'm on my back again. Fuckit! Anger can occasionally fuel the will. Roll the body over to one side, hoisting instead of hauling, left elbow taking the full weight as legs are inched over the side of the bed. A moment's pain as the weight shifts to the lower back, but almost at once I'm upright. Sitting, breathless with the effort of it, in pitch-black darkness – my feet are flat on the floor and I'm triumphant.

Victor is still snoring but not as evenly as before, and I wait till the snorts regain a rhythm before sliding to the edge of the bed. I let my head drop forward, and complete the momentum that takes me off the bed and on to my feet. Hurrah! I breathe deeply.

Next: the shuffle to the door, trying to remember the obstacles, shoes pulled off and dumped, clothes lying where they were dropped, a chair, not to mention the creaky board by the door, and being sure to step sideways, crab-style, over the threshold, so it doesn't freeze me. Along the corridor to the kitchen, feeling my way towards the sink where I switch on a tiny lamp, giving just enough light to see to make tea.

I stand dozily, waiting for the kettle to boil, one hip balancing me against the sink. Something outside catches my attention, breaks in. A sudden flicker through the trees in the square, as if someone has lit a cigarette. I imagine a deep draw, a pleasure long postponed, and the almost instantaneous kickback of guilt: whoever it is at once throws the cigarette to the ground and steps on it, since after that momentary flicker I see nothing more. I stare at the spot and seem to make out a black streak of a shadow which moves as if about to form into a figure, but then doesn't materialise. My apparition. I've come to think of him as the ghost of Doctor P. who, two hundred years ago, walked in the streets just south of mine and observed persons he saw to be afflicted with the disease he defined. His essay hardly touches me now. It's as if I've developed a way of comprehending his account while somehow not applying it to my own case, as if a layer of cotton wool protects my raw nerves from the full imaginative impact of his words.

His appearances have become so fleeting that I sometimes wonder if he exists at all other than as an apparently materialising shadow, a hallucination. Perhaps he's not Doctor P. but one of the solitary walkers, those who feel most themselves walking the streets. They might be seen anywhere, at any hour, in all weathers. They live to walk, and it's as if their survival depends on it, not only to dull some long-suffered pain of existence with the routine of physical exertion, but because, by the implicit offering of their goodwill to everyone they pass, they bestow grace on them, and find their own justification. Most people are blind to them, these guardian angels, but a few who are aware beyond their own concerns will notice the reappearance of the same walker again and again, as if he – or she – is tracking them. As the years pass they come to look out for him, even to acknowledge him. They see him age and slow, and then they see him rarely and then not at all, but it might be months before they note his absence and feel sorrow at his passing.

I focus again on the place in the trees, but nothing moves now; if he was there, he's gone.

I make a slow progression along the corridor to the room that's Victor's studio, bearing the cup of tea as if in an egg and spoon race. Victor, mildly regretful of the stains on the carpet, has suggested a tray, which is one thing too many to consider, so I move carefully, inching forwards, not to let my feet run away with me. I pull open the door, and slow to a creep in case I freeze to the spot, which can happen at any kind of threshold, as if I've come up against a brick wall. Stopping and starting, the clash of opposing forces, an implosion, from frozen in my tracks to an agitated run forwards – so that if I stop I can't start again, and once started, I can't stop.

Reaching the daybed, I place the tea on the table. Then I turn too abruptly so my feet stick and I start to topple, but I'm close enough to the bed to fall on it. I close my eyes. The sense of homecoming is so intense that a sob catches my breath.

Once, I railed against my short nights, but I've come to see that they suit me, and now I depend for my wellbeing on the two or three hours of quiet contemplation my insomnia allows me. I've even stopped thinking of it as insomnia. It's a time of clarity, the drug-free hours.

Victor has given me a corner of his studio to use in

the night. Behind a screen is a daybed with a small table beside it. Every evening I prepare the bed, so that I can slip quickly under the blanket and, sipping a cup of tea, consider the books and papers on the little round table at my side. I'm cocooned by the light from a lamp on the floor behind me, and the room beyond the screen with its chaos of canvasses, piles of drawings, the plastic carrier bags in which Victor keeps his papers, the many images tacked to the walls, is lost in velvety blackness. Just as the world beyond is lost in silence. Only the smell penetrates to my corner, the heady, nose-tingling fumes of turpentine that overwhelm the gentler taste of tea. And then, my cup empty, I read, or, sometimes, write. If it is writing. Moving paragraphs around on a computer on my lap, stiffly, haltingly tapping out words which mostly I then discard – is this writing? I've still things to write about Belle, my companion through these years of Doctor P., but I keep putting off the moment when I might finish. It's partly the business of the house. I came across an etching of the house Belle lived in with Charles, a large house made pretentious by its gracelessness, an ugly house in what looks like the scrappy outskirts of a town. I was oddly distressed by this discovery. I had posited my Belle on the idea of a house of heart-stopping beauty, a wonder, on the edge of a village deep in the countryside and now that I'm faced with the reality I fear for the integrity of my view of her.

But it's not only that. I've put it off also because to write The End would be to invite my own. Now it may be too late, this malady has dried up my juices; and when I look at these fragments of writing I see a mind that is stuck. This stuckness has become the chief attribute of my condition, in various manifestations.

My fingers stick on the keyboard. My feet stick to the floor. My mind sticks in a groove, as if the range of possible associated thoughts is narrowing. I or my brain can't stray from a few well-trodden paths, and digs an ever deepening and engulfing furrow, a pit of obsession. What's to be done? I can't stop it, but perhaps I can make something of it. Put it to use. Turn it to gold.

A figure looms out of the darkness beyond the screen. Victor stands there in his pyjamas.

'So I woke you?'

He yawns in answer.

'You were asleep when I left.'

'Only pretending to be.'

'That was a very convincing snore.'

'So it was me who woke us?'

'Who knows? I don't expect so.'

'Are you working? You shouldn't work. You should lie quietly, concentrate on the pineal eye.'

'I'm lying here quietly, minding my own business.'

'Can I join you?'

I would rather he doesn't, knowing how it's likely to end, with his snoring beside me on the too small daybed, so I have to go back to the bedroom.

'You're too cavalier about this sleeplessness, it's bad for you.' He climbs in beside me and we lie quietly for a while.

I consider how it is between us, Victor and me, how different, though also the same, as if we've picked up where we left off but with a new sense of the fragility of what we have, how easily it can be broken and how much we want to keep it whole.

Anna just came for a visit. We took her on a walk along the south bank. She was full of little attentions, well-meant undoubtedly, but unwelcome to me, since I was fully drugged, as was surely evident, and didn't need Anna to fetch and carry for me. She was kind, she was thoughtful – but not so kind and thoughtful as to perceive what was really required.

I was already irritated when we got out of the lift at the top of the Oxo tower and I had an attack of vertigo. Not only did I feel in danger of throwing myself over the railing, but I feared for Victor and Anna too, and urged them back from the edge. But later, on a terrace at the Tate, I wasn't affected, which Victor said was peculiar, and Anna thought so too, as if I was guilty of inconsistency, as if they knew nothing about vertigo, how it took one differently at different times, and according to subtle differences in the location. (The vantage point at the Oxo tower juts outwards while the terrace at the Tate is enclosed on three sides.) I suggested that they carry on together while I returned to Anna's car and waited. Anna disagreed: we should carry on together, and if I got tired she would go and fetch the car; but Victor, who had had enough, wanted us all to go back to the car. So Anna said that I, as the invalid I suppose, should decide, and they would do what I wanted. But when I again voiced my preference, she insisted on her own plan.

It's always a struggle, and a temptation: to make illness my role, my identifying characteristic, rather than just another fact of life, however I might internalise it. I could have controlled my highly strung if not hysterical reaction to the drop from the Oxo tower, I didn't have to impose my vertigo on the others. And Victor was right when he said it was all a comedy, and the only thing to do was to laugh.

I laugh, and Victor beside me stirs. 'What's funny?'

'I'm thinking about yesterday, Anna and all that.'

'I'm glad you can laugh.'

'It was silly. But she's too much. Perhaps I am too.'

'Anna's Anna. We know how she is by now. And you – well, we know you too.'

Yes, a woman who's become cranky, with her ticks and manias. A woman who doesn't look old but has many of the signs of age: a slight unsteadiness and stiffness, a smile that has to be forced, a faint voice with blurry articulation, and in general a manner that is indefinably odd, that jars when frailty breaks through a surface normality.

I wonder if Victor is nodding off until I feel his hand finding a way in through my sweater and then undoing the buttons of my nightdress, finding my breasts. I need the drugs for this, the drugs that stop me writing in the day time, dry up those juices, allow these ones to flow. Still, I seek his penis, which is stiff against my side, and fumble because my hand is clumsy, but though I can't work my best magic, I run one finger, as gentle as gossamer, deep into the central place he likes it best, and stroke him too from behind, my head on his chest, and soon he comes with a groan. But then, as he sighs happily and stretches out, he rolls with a little shout off the side of the daybed, and we both begin to laugh. He hoists himself back, and still laughing I make room for him, and we settle down in a squashed heap. Soon he begins to snore, but gently, little more than a whispering sigh that will surely lull me into sleep.

I picture Belle towards the end of her life, sitting at her desk, with her back to the window, not to be distracted by the view up the valley, reserved for naps on the daybed. Not long ago I came across a passage in a letter that I must have missed or was blind to in previous readings: 'I never came back to the place without a sense of despair. I determined then never to leave it. And I have rendered it endurable.' I count the years: eighteen. Shut away with Charles and his sisters, in a house that had become a prison, and all the more confining because her life sentence was self-imposed.

I see her form as if from the garden: upswept hair on her bowed head so her neck is revealed above a voile collar. A woman of excellence and distinction, who has committed herself to her work and will whatever the restraints on her freedom remain loyal to it till the end.

But something is hindering her, and it's more than fits of sleep. Her quarrel with Benjamin perhaps: he accused her of being squeamish about the revolution, insisting that you were either for the people or against them, and it was no good wanting change and balking at the consequences. He told her too, when she objected to his taking up with the Necker woman, that she, Belle, was smothering him. She had always been tolerant of his mistresses, even made a pet of his wife, so long as she (Belle again) remained his intellectual mainstay. Now Necker had stolen her role, or Benjamin had conferred it on her. Belle, who could ill afford to lose him, made it the breaking point, and pride dictated that the rupture come from her: 'I like neither your way of life nor your friends, neither your politics nor the politics of those with you, and I have no wish to argue with you any more. You are no longer my kind of person.' Or perhaps not, perhaps she was done with Benjamin. There were so many others, young men and women, queuing up to sit at her feet –

and if none had his gifts, which once chimed so sympathetically with her own, well – she shrugged and hauled herself to her feet. And now the letters were getting in her way, his and everyone else's, so many of them, in boxes stacked around her desk – she knocked one over and the contents were strewn across the floor. Wasn't she hemmed in by so much past?

The irresistible pull of the daybed in the late afternoon. She'd abandon the struggle for now – to write, to keep her eyes open. Another half-hour and Ruth would bring the tea things, and find her stretched out under her plaid rug, asleep.

I reach for a notebook. I'm thinking now about spaces. Ideal spaces, to live in, to live a perfect life in, to be calm and good in. I'm thinking of a place without particular entrances or exits, in which spaces take the place of rooms, spaces that emerge out of and into other spaces, that are shaped rather than angled, curved rather than cornered, some inside and some out; in which windows and doors are set wherever there's a notable view, of gardens tended or city streets, or the light is especially advantageous. These spaces have no particular functions, and a person might lie down to sleep on one of several daybeds, sit down to eat or work at any of the many tables. A stove in the centre of one of these spaces would supply heat and cooking facilities, and a bathroom, placed at one or other end of the sequence, would take a more pronounced curve so as to be made private. Gentle, organic, continuous forms, snaking across landscapes, would make for a world without beginnings or endings, starts or stops, or wieldings of power and possession – on and on and on.

My name is Lin

'M-M-My name is Lin.'
  'Louder.'
  'M-MY NAME IS LIN.'
  'Give it some shape: my name is *Lin*.'
  'My Name Is *L-L-Lin*.'
  'OK. Where do you live?'
  'I live in London.'
  'Project – as if you're throwing me a ball.'
  'I-I-I LIVE IN LONDON.'
  'Loud enough but now give it some variation.'
  'I L-LIVE IN LonDON.'
  'LONdon.'
  'LONdon.'
  'Better. Now, say after me, "Listen to a Londoner called Lin – "'
  'Listen to a Londoner called Lin – '
  '– speak.'
  'SPEAK.'

LENZ
books